KU-169-199

—TAKE 5—
CROSSWORDS

igloobooks

igloobooks

Published in 2023
First published in the UK by Igloo Books Ltd
An imprint of Igloo Books Ltd
Cottage Farm, NN6 0BJ, UK
Owned by Bonnier Books
Sveavägen 56, Stockholm, Sweden
www.igloobooks.com

Copyright © 2022 Igloo Books Ltd

All rights reserved. No part of this publication may be
reproduced or transmitted in any form or by any means,
electronic, or mechanical, including photocopying, recording,
or by any information storage and retrieval system,
without permission in writing from the publisher.

0523 001
2 4 6 8 10 9 7 5 3 1
ISBN 978-1-83795-326-4

Puzzle compilation, typesetting and design by:
Clarity Media Ltd, http://www.clarity-media.co.uk

Printed and manufactured in the UK

Contents

No 1

	L¹	I²	N	G³	U	I⁴	S⁵	T	I	C⁶	S	
7												8
				9						10	F	A	R
11	T	R	O									
							12	J	U	S	H	I
13												
						14	S		15			
				16	17		T					
18		19		20			I					
						21	C					
22				23	G	R	E	E	K			
							E					
	24						R					

Across

- **1** Phraseology (11)
- **9** Nosed (anag) (5)
- **10** Not near (3)
- **11** Prize (5)
- **12** Japanese food (5)
- **13** Lower (8)
- **16** Sport (8)
- **18** Encounters (5)
- **21** Crave; desire (5)
- **22** Take or steal something (3)
- **23** Eg from Athens (5)
- **24** Daring; bold (11)

Down

- **2** Improve (7)
- **3** Inclination (7)
- **4** Pokes gently (6)
- **5** Endures (5)
- **6** Presents (5)
- **7** Promising; budding (2-3-6)
- **8** Hinged; segmented (11)
- **14** Adhesive label (7)
- **15** Upstart; one who has recently gained wealth (7)
- **17** East (6)
- **19** Implant (5)
- **20** Smooth transition (5)

No 2

Across

1 Swiss city (6)
7 Impeccable (8)
8 Eg English Breakfast (3)
9 Adjusting the pitch of a musical instrument (6)
10 Vehicle pulled by a horse (4)
11 Perhaps (5)
13 Width (7)
15 Poked (7)
17 Smells strongly (5)
21 Cameron ___ : actress (4)
22 Prowler (6)
23 Consumed food (3)
24 Graceful (of movement) (8)
25 Set out on a journey (6)

Down

1 ___ City: where Batman lives (6)
2 Tidily (6)
3 Attach (5)
4 Nocturnal burrowing mammals (7)
5 Obstruction (8)
6 Sprightliness (6)
12 Greatly impress (8)
14 Abundantly supplied (7)
16 Nasal (6)
18 Mistakes in printed matter (6)
19 Long thin line or band (6)
20 Device used to give support (5)

No 3

Across

1. Office furniture (4)
3. Abstract ideas (8)
9. Item of clerical clothing (7)
10. Health professional (5)
11. Airing a TV program (12)
14. Was in first place (3)
16. Turf out (5)
17. Exclamation of surprise (3)
18. Absurd (12)
21. Moderate and well-balanced (5)
22. Polygon having ten sides (7)
23. City in NE Scotland (8)
24. Midge (4)

Down

1. Sound units (8)
2. US R&B singer (5)
4. Tree of the genus Quercus (3)
5. Body of voters in a given area (12)
6. Predatory fish (7)
7. Takes to court (4)
8. Easy-going (4-8)
12. Operatic songs (5)
13. Dark reddish-brown colour (8)
15. Very long lasting (7)
19. Church instrument (5)
20. Continent (4)
22. Expected at a certain time (3)

1 desk?

21. Level

No 4

Across

1 Prizes (6)
4 Respect and admire (6)
9 Big shot; head honcho (7)
10 Chilled desserts (7)
11 Puts in order (5)
12 Conceals (5)
14 States to be the case (5)
15 Chasm (5)
17 Spanish wine (5)
18 Art of paper-folding (7)
20 Land with fruit trees (7)
21 Jumped in the air (6)
22 Far from the target (6)

Down

1 Birthplace of St Francis (6)
2 Harshness of manner (8)
3 Judges (5)
5 Eg Poirot and Sherlock Holmes (7)
6 Flightless birds (4)
7 Church services (6)
8 Sponsor mice (anag) (11)
13 Suave; stylish (8)
14 With an attitude of suspicion (7)
15 Open declaration of affirmation (6)
16 Barely (6)
17 Moves back and forth (5)
19 Thought (4)

No 5

Across

1 Diminished in size (6)
7 Speculative (8)
8 Dry and mocking (3)
9 Fibre from the angora goat (6)
10 Justin ___ : golfer who won the 2013 US Open (4)
11 Finished (5)
13 Working at a loom (7)
15 Soothsayer (7)
17 Personal attendant (5)
21 Neither good nor bad (2-2)
22 Starting point (6)
23 Annoy (3)
24 Greasiness (8)
25 Twist together (6)

Down

1 Waste matter (6)
2 Had corresponding sounds (6)
3 Manipulate dough (5)
4 Began (7)
5 Capital of Liberia (8)
6 Nigella ___ : English food writer (6)
12 Elation (8)
14 Avid follower (7)
16 Novice (6)
18 Protective layer (6)
19 Excite agreeably (6)
20 Damien ___ : modern English artist (5)

No 6

Across

1 Sturdy motor vehicles (5)
4 Move from one place to another (5)
10 Japanese flower arranging (7)
11 Show indifference with the shoulders (5)
12 Route (4)
13 Elastic (8)
16 Lethargic; sleepy (6)
17 Investigated in detail (6)
20 Affecting only the appearance (8)
21 Metallic element (4)
23 Promotional wording (5)
25 To the same degree (7)
26 Vacillate (5)
27 Sends an SMS (5)

Down

2 Efforts (9)
3 Participate in a game (4)
5 Inn (8)
6 Evergreen coniferous tree (3)
7 Torn (of clothes) (6)
8 Ray (5)
9 ___ bread: French toast (4)
14 Car with a folding roof (9)
15 Gather together in one place (8)
18 Metrical foot (6)
19 Vertical part of a step (5)
20 Young lions (4)
22 Horse and donkey offspring (4)
24 ___ Thurman: Hollywood star (3)

Grid (with handwritten answers):

Left margin letters (top to bottom): A B B R E V I A T I O N S

- 1A: **A B B R** (ABBREVIATIONS written down the left side)
- 1 Across / Down answers filled in:
  - 1A **A**
  - **B**
  - 9 **B R**
  - 11 **B R E N T** (BRENT)
  - 12
  - 13 **I D E A L S**
  - 14 **A**
  - 17 **T** / **I**
  - 18 **W A T E R** (18 across) with 19 down **H I G**
  - 20 **S H A R K** / **N**
  - 22 **S T E A L I N G** / 23 **W H E T**

Across

1 Having pains (4)
3 Shackle (8) HANDCUF?
9 Cookie (7)
10 Chocolate powder (5)
11 Upright (5) ✓
12 Release (7)
13 Personal principles (6)
15 Danish monetary unit (pl) (6)
17 Cheep (7)
18 Levy (5)
20 Fish-eating mammal (5) ✓
21 Travelling very quickly (7) zooming
22 Robbing (8) ✓
23 Stimulate the appetite (4) ✓

Down

1 Shortened forms of words (13)
2 Hermann ___ : author of Steppenwolf (5)
4 ___ Conan Doyle: author (6)
5 Act of slowing down (12)
6 Liberate; release (7)
7 Boxing class division (13)
8 Agreed upon by several parties (12)
14 Letter (7)
16 Shamelessly bold (6)
19 Upper part of the leg (5) ✓

∧   WATER

No 8

Across

8 Of one mind (9)
9 Gone by (3)
10 Wash one's body in water (5)
11 Soft suede leather (7)
12 French bean (7)
13 Seal of the Archbishop of York (4)
17 Bristle (4)
18 Supreme fleet commander (7)
22 Summary of events (5-2)
24 Furnishings of a room (5)
25 Source of a metal (3)
26 Farm machines (9)

Down

1 Married man (informal) (5)
2 Highly seasoned smoked beef (8)
3 Relating to motion (7)
4 Mexican cloak (6)
5 English homework assignment (5)
6 Burkina ___ : African country (4)
7 Shaving of the crown of head (7)
14 Split into subdivisions (8)
15 Cigar (7)
16 Least tame (7)
19 Extradite (6)
20 Amends (5)
21 Secret rendezvous (5)
23 Employs (4)

No 9

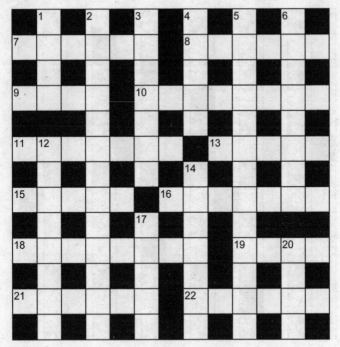

Across

7 Residents of an area (6)
8 Long for (6)
9 Scottish singer-songwriter (4)
10 Knitted jacket (8)
11 Live together (7)
13 Portion of a play (5)
15 Looks good on (5)
16 Complicated (7)
18 Overly anxious and sensitive (8)
19 Small symbol or graphic (4)
21 Son of Daedalus in Greek mythology (6)
22 Event which precedes another (6)

Down

1 Soya bean curd (4)
2 Makers (13)
3 Able to read minds (7)
4 Predatory marine fish (5)
5 Lacking in control (13)
6 Someone in custody (8)
12 Wealth (8)
14 General idea (7)
17 Secret store of something (5)
20 Roman poet (4)

No 10

Across

1 ___ Sharif: Egyptian actor (4)
3 Drink consumed before bed (8)
9 Molasses (7)
10 Social gathering (5)
11 Form of deception (12)
14 A knight (3)
16 In a ___ : very quickly (5)
17 Pointed tool (3)
18 Brutally; harshly (12)
21 Declaration (5)
22 Kitchen implement (7)
23 Cambridge vs Oxford event (4-4)
24 Anti-aircraft fire (4)

Down

1 Opposite of a pessimist (8)
2 Regions (5)
4 Frozen water (3)
5 Conjectural (12)
6 Bodies of writing (7)
7 Yaps (anag) (4)
8 Author of screenplays (12)
12 Makes (a sound) (5)
13 Reproduce recorded sound (4,4)
15 Copy (7)
19 Be the same as (5)
20 Action word (4)
22 Intentionally so written (3)

No 11

Across

1 Occupancy (11)
9 Senior figure in a tribe (5)
10 22nd Greek letter (3)
11 Electronic communication (5)
12 A woolly ruminant animal (5)
13 Cowards (8)
16 Fugitives (8)
18 Wireless (5)
21 Pollex (5)
22 Purpose (3)
23 Decay (5)
24 Founded (11)

Down

2 ___ Portman: actress (7)
3 Simian (7)
4 Eg from New Delhi (6)
5 Large amounts of land (5)
6 A hidden storage space (5)
7 Traitorous (11)
8 Unnecessary; superfluous (11)
14 Hurries (7)
15 Caribbean dance (7)
17 Large group of fish (6)
19 Workers (5)
20 Last Greek letter (5)

No 12

Across

1 Caress (6)
4 Pertaining to vinegar (6)
9 Of the stomach (7)
10 Bumped into (7)
11 Natural elevation (5)
12 George ___ : Middlemarch writer (5)
14 Scraped at (of an animal) (5)
15 Pilfer (5)
17 Soft lustre on a surface (5)
18 Trialled or tested (7)
20 Igneous rock (7)
21 Limp (6)
22 Approached (6)

Down

1 Body shape (6)
2 Plummet (8)
3 Huge (5)
5 Not straight (7)
6 Bloodsucking insect (4)
7 Recognition (6)
8 Admit to be true (11)
13 Of lower quality (8)
14 Humorous; done in fun (7)
15 Sledge (6)
16 Have as a purpose (6)
17 Induce fear (5)
19 Absorbent pad (4)

No 13

Across

8 Manner of acting (9)
9 Large dark antelope (3)
10 Large woody plants (5)
11 Look after an infant (7)
12 Eg fluorine or chlorine (7)
13 Capital of the Ukraine (4)
17 Bovine animals (4)
18 Nimbleness (7)
22 Communal settlement in Israel (7)
24 The prevailing fashion (5)
25 One and one (3)
26 Quivering (9)

Down

1 Assists in a crime (5)
2 Cord for fastening footwear (8)
3 Avoidance (7)
4 ___ Williams: singer (6)
5 Illegal payment (5)
6 Grows older (4)
7 Sly (7)
14 An engraved design (8)
15 Projectile fireworks (7)
16 Pertaining to a river (7)
19 Small garden building (6)
20 Shapely (5)
21 Condescend (5)
23 Sudden misfortune (4)

No 14

Across

1 Top aim (anag) (6)
7 Leave of absence (8)
8 Single in number (3)
9 Andy ___ : British tennis star (6)
10 Merriment (4)
11 Teams (5)
13 Shut in (7)
15 Washing sponges (7)
17 Old-fashioned (5)
21 Sharp bites (4)
22 Snared (6)
23 ___ Botham: former cricketer (3)
24 Laugh uproariously (8)
25 Less quiet (6)

Down

1 Smells (6)
2 Rained heavily (6)
3 Burning (5)
4 Wax sticks used for drawing (7)
5 Country of East Asia (8)
6 A way out (6)
12 Overflowing with praise (8)
14 Coarse beach gravel (7)
16 Prayer (6)
18 Cleaned up (6)
19 Main meal (6)
20 Iron alloy (5)

No 15

Across

1 Grammatical case in Latin (8)
5 Country in South America (4)
8 Edible seaweed (5)
9 Makes ineffective (7)
10 Volcanic crater (7)
12 Hot pepper (7)
14 Modernised (7)
16 Operating doctor (7)
18 Preventing success; unfavourable (7)
19 Lazy person (5)
20 Soft drink (US) (4)
21 Wild flower (8)

Down

1 Dell (4)
2 Hollow in a solid object (6)
3 Finish (9)
4 City in NE Italy (6)
6 One or the other of two (6)
7 Not closed (of an envelope) (8)
11 Overwhelming majority of votes for one party (9)
12 Solids with regularly ordered atoms (8)
13 Showed to be true (6)
14 Imaginary (6)
15 Number of Apostles (6)
17 By word of mouth (4)

No 16

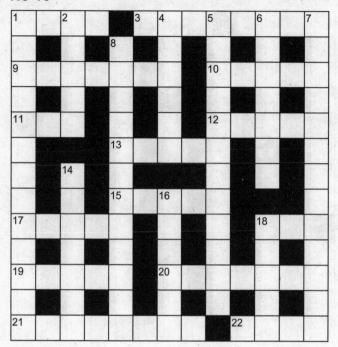

Across

1 Clever remark (4)
3 Progresses (8)
9 Ancient large storage jar (7)
10 Type of plastic (5)
11 Climbing shrub (3)
12 Mother-of-pearl (5)
13 Vault under a church (5)
15 Glazed earthenware (5)
17 Ornamental stone (5)
18 Signal for action (3)
19 Data entered into a system (5)
20 Epicure (7)
21 Unnecessary (8)
22 Mimic (4)

Down

1 Accomplishment making one suitable for a job (13)
2 State indirectly (5)
4 Very much (6)
5 Coming from outside (12)
6 Distrustful of sincerity (7)
7 Obviously (4-9)
8 Occurring at the same time (12)
14 Crush underfoot (7)
16 Small houses (6)
18 Brief appearance (5)

No 17

Across

1 School test (4)
3 Give someone the courage to do something (8)
9 Saying (7)
10 The Hunter (constellation) (5)
11 Intolerable (12)
14 Shola ___ : singer (3)
16 A leaf of paper (5)
17 Hair colourant (3)
18 Malice ___ : intention to harm (12)
21 Porcelain (5)
22 Army unit (7)
23 Remaining (8)
24 Large deer (pl) (4)

Down

1 Marriage ceremony (8)
2 Smell (5)
4 Gang (3)
5 Use of words that mimic sounds (12)
6 Bored into (7)
7 One less than ten (4)
8 From this time on (12)
12 Person who flies an aircraft (5)
13 Tidiness (8)
15 Business matters (7)
19 Holy chalice (5)
20 Skin mark from a wound (4)
22 Bleat of a sheep (3)

No 18

Across

1 Apple seeds (4)
3 Range of colours (8)
9 Writing fluid holder (7)
10 Mountain range in South America (5)
11 Main artery (5)
12 From beginning to end (7)
13 Root vegetable (6)
15 Bump against roughly (6)
17 Newness (7)
18 Friend (Spanish) (5)
20 Business proposal; playing field (5)
21 Accumulates over time (7)
22 Publisher's emblem (8)
23 Refuse to obey; rebel against (4)

Down

1 Benevolent and generous (13)
2 Card game (5)
4 Roof of the mouth (6)
5 Ability to see the future (12)
6 Enclosed fortification (7)
7 Naughtily (13)
8 Connection or association (12)
14 Musical performance (7)
16 Extremely energetic person (6)
19 Accustom (5)

No 19

Across

1 Unwell (4)
3 Succession; series (8)
9 Be subjected to (7)
10 Mature human (5)
11 Device for putting out fires (12)
13 Very cold (of weather) (6)
15 Cloud of gas in space (6)
17 Awe-inspiring (12)
20 Service colour of the army (5)
21 Assemble; gather (7)
22 Narrow street or passage (8)
23 Celestial body (4)

Down

1 Cooking pot (8)
2 Military trainee (5)
4 Exit; Bible book (6)
5 Not capable of reply (12)
6 Art ___ : decorative style of art (7)
7 Consumes (4)
8 Eg Wales (12)
12 Female offspring (8)
14 Cut short (7)
16 Modern ballroom dance (3-3)
18 Clumsy (5)
19 Gull-like bird (4)

22

No 20

Across

1 Attack with severe criticism (6)
5 Where one finds Oslo (6)
8 Scorch (4)
9 11th month of the year (8)
10 A finger or toe (5)
11 Subsiding (7)
14 Spite (13)
16 Feeling guilty (7)
18 Mammal of the weasel family (5)
20 Ability to act as one wishes (4,4)
22 Falls behind (4)
23 Where bread is made (6)
24 Misplace (6)

Down

2 Eg ammonia and caustic soda (9)
3 Stations at the ends of routes (7)
4 Volcano in Sicily (4)
5 Dark colour that is virtually black (4,4)
6 Send money (5)
7 Affirmative vote (3)
12 Longing for something past (9)
13 Faithfulness (8)
15 Stinging plants (7)
17 ___ Adkins: singer (5)
19 Dejected (4)
21 Chris ___ : English singer (3)

No 21

Across

1 Speak in a confused way (6)
4 Customary practices (6)
9 ___ Potter: English author (7)
10 Combined metals (7)
11 Very bad (5)
12 More than enough (5)
14 Remove wool from sheep (5)
15 Paula ___ : US singer (5)
17 Crazy (5)
18 Very old (7)
20 Sets out on a journey (7)
21 State of mental strain (6)
22 Extreme confusion (6)

Down

1 Talk foolishly (6)
2 Calculated and careful (8)
3 Truck (5)
5 Relating to a star (7)
6 Dull colour (4)
7 Quash; tame (6)
8 Overstated (11)
13 Pertaining to the chest (8)
14 Protective CD covers (7)
15 Adjusts (6)
16 Mineral used to make plaster of Paris (6)
17 ___ gas: eg neon or argon (5)
19 Singe; burn (4)

No 22

Across

1. Discover (6)
7. Send to a different place (8)
8. By way of (3)
9. Hot pepper (6)
10. Converse (4)
11. ___ Beckford: US fashion model (5)
13. Obtained from a source (7)
15. Become airborne (4,3)
17. Anxiety (5)
21. Celebration; festivity (4)
22. Lament (6)
23. Cooling tool (3)
24. Tepid (8)
25. Pottery fragments (6)

Down

1. Deprive of power (6)
2. Follows the position of (6)
3. Mythical monster (5)
4. Suitor (7)
5. Force of resistance; abrasion (8)
6. Colourless hydrocarbon (6)
12. Uses a piece of machinery (8)
14. Unconventional (7)
16. Calculating machine (6)
18. Eg Rory McIlroy (6)
19. Main tree stems (6)
20. Propels the body through water (5)

No 23

Across

1 Lacking confidence (8)
5 Have a ___ at: attempt (4)
9 Language of the Romans (5)
10 Relating to country life (5)
11 Causing great anxiety (4-6)
14 Wears away (6)
15 State publicly (6)
17 On the record; formally (10)
20 Relay device (5)
21 Golden ___ : bird of prey (5)
22 Depart (4)
23 Squander money (8)

Down

1 La ___ Bonita: Madonna hit (4)
2 Locate or place (4)
3 Person recovering from an illness (12)
4 Remember (6)
6 Fantastic (8)
7 Eg rugby or tennis (4,4)
8 Productivity (12)
12 Make more intense (8)
13 Coloured paper thrown at weddings (8)
16 Type of sandwich (6)
18 Fever (4)
19 Grain that grows into a new plant (4)

No 24

Across

1 Passage (4)
3 Complying with orders (8)
9 Health and fortunes of a group (7)
10 Name applied to something (5)
11 Having an acrid wit (5-7)
14 Broken equipment (3)
16 Remorse (5)
17 ___ Barker: former tennis star (3)
18 Afraid to speak frankly (5-7)
21 Simple (5)
22 Mark the boundaries of (7)
23 Delaying (8)
24 Extent of a surface (4)

Down

1 Negative aspect (8)
2 Eyelashes (5)
4 Insect that can sting (3)
5 Charmingly (12)
6 Symbolic objects (7)
7 Chat (4)
8 Carefree (5-2-5)
12 General hatred (5)
13 Feud (8)
15 Piece of furniture (7)
19 Bart's father in the Simpsons (5)
20 Touch (4)
22 Secret retreat (3)

No 25

Across

1 Papal representative (6)
4 Return on investment (6)
9 Group of figures representing a scene (7)
10 Large dark low cloud (7)
11 Spends time doing nothing (5)
12 Pastime (5)
14 Make good on a debt (5)
15 Important question (5)
17 ___ Izzard: stand-up comedian (5)
18 Move; agitate (7)
20 Makes untidy with rubbish (7)
21 Eagles' nests (6)
22 Doze (6)

Down

1 Foolish person (6)
2 Indistinct; hazy (8)
3 Individual things (5)
5 State of lawlessness (7)
6 Kiln for drying hops (4)
7 Playful; energetic (6)
8 Vulnerable to (11)
13 Short heavy club (8)
14 Rise again (7)
15 Bring about (6)
16 Botch (4-2)
17 Background actor (5)
19 Engage in argument (4)

No 26

Across

1 True information (4)
3 Charm (8)
9 Hereditary title (7)
10 Extinct birds (5)
11 Inadequately manned (12)
13 Withdraw; gradually diminish (6)
15 Hard substance that covers teeth (6)
17 Science of biological processes (12)
20 Greeting (5)
21 Vent for molten lava (7)
22 Enclosed area in a farm (8)
23 Read quickly (4)

Down

1 Second month (8)
2 Felt concern or interest (5)
4 Sagacious (6)
5 Not capable of justification (12)
6 Trimmed (anag) (7)
7 Prying (4)
8 Preliminary (12)
12 Recreational area for children (8)
14 Device for cooling (7)
16 Type of craftsman (6)
18 Express gratitude (5)
19 Freshwater game fish (4)

No 27

Across

1 Approximate (8)
5 Apparatus for weaving (4)
8 Thing that imparts motion (5)
9 Settled in advance (7)
10 Rupert ___ : English actor (7)
12 Halted (7)
14 Bicycle stunt (7)
16 Tom Jones song (7)
18 Raging fire (7)
19 Island in the Mediterranean Sea (5)
20 Current of air (4)
21 Ignominy; dishonour (8)

Down

1 Prestigious TV award (4)
2 Stain skin with indelible colour (6)
3 Mammal with a pouch (9)
4 Eclipsed (6)
6 Speaks publicly (6)
7 Think deeply for a period of time (8)
11 Surpassing (9)
12 Reading carefully (8)
13 Feigns (6)
14 ___ Goldberg: US actress (6)
15 Thin layer of sedimentary rock (6)
17 Strong and healthy (4)

No 28

Across

1 Drink copiously (5)
4 Contrary to (7)
7 Irritate (5)
8 Educating (8)
9 Warhorse (5)
11 Hot and humid (8)
15 Showing embarrassment (8)
17 Incision; indent (5)
19 Loud and harsh (8)
20 Russian monarchs (5)
21 Showed a person to their seat (7)
22 Interruption (5)

Down

1 Citation (9)
2 Pilot (7)
3 Vivid purplish-red colour (7)
4 ___ Holden: English actress (6)
5 Inborn (6)
6 Large pebble (5)
10 Contrast between two things (9)
12 Deserved (7)
13 Open-minded; given freely (7)
14 Rarely encountered (6)
16 Intense dislike (6)
18 Fertile area in a desert (5)

No 29

Across

1 Mature people (6)
7 Teachers (anag) (8)
8 Tropical constrictor (3)
9 Pasta strip (6)
10 Simple non-flowering plant (4)
11 Unexpected catches (5)
13 Flowering shrubs (7)
15 Charm; enchant (7)
17 ___ Dumbledore: Harry Potter character (5)
21 Proofreader's mark (4)
22 Shining (6)
23 Hog (3)
24 Aromatic herb (8)
25 Pleasant and agreeable (6)

Down

1 Superior of a nunnery (6)
2 Country once ruled by Idi Amin (6)
3 Of doubtful honesty (5)
4 Musical movements (7)
5 Similarity (8)
6 Figure of speech (6)
12 Shiny; sparkly (8)
14 Thin and bony (7)
16 Background actors (6)
18 Knocked into (6)
19 Unkempt (of hair) (6)
20 Open and close the eyes quickly (5)

No 30

Across

1 Curved shape (4)
3 Formal speeches (8)
9 Windpipe (7)
10 Angry (5)
11 Not intoxicating (of a drink) (12)
14 Floor covering (3)
16 The reproduction of sound (5)
17 Beer (3)
18 Outsmart (12)
21 Pertaining to bees (5)
22 Flight hub (7)
23 Country one lives in (8)
24 Watchful; awry (anag) (4)

Down

1 Right to self-government (8)
2 Series of linked metal rings (5)
4 Long and narrow inlet (3)
5 Mathematics of triangles (12)
6 Musical wind instrument (7)
7 Look for (4)
8 Devoted to music (12)
12 ___ days: long ago (5)
13 Not long ago (8)
15 Activity of travelling for pleasure (7)
19 Musical instrument (5)
20 Beach constituent (4)
22 Trouble in body or mind (3)

No 31

Across

7 Overcome a difficulty (8)
8 Rain (anag) (4)
9 Flightless bird (4)
10 Deserving blame (8)
11 Toxin in the body (7)
12 Things you buy; effects (5)
15 Dark wood (5)
17 Act of touching (7)
20 Position of a male monarch (8)
22 Type of golf club (4)
23 Molten rock (4)
24 Cross-bred dogs (8)

Down

1 Swelling on the big toe (6)
2 Aspiration (8)
3 Become faster (7)
4 Took illegally (5)
5 ___ Turner: US singer (4)
6 Incarcerated (6)
13 Complete (8)
14 Pennies (7)
16 Relating to a wedding (6)
18 Musical ensembles (6)
19 Cool down (5)
21 Delighted (4)

No 32

Across

1 Access illegally (4)
3 Climbed (8)
9 Having a large belly (7)
10 Precipice (5)
11 Refute by evidence (5)
12 Difficult to catch (7)
13 Putrid (6)
15 Fine cloth; type of paper (6)
17 Quiver (7)
18 Short treatise (5)
20 Papal court (5)
21 Ice cream flavour (7)
22 Popular fizzy beverage (8)
23 Computer memory unit (4)

Down

1 Excessively negative about (13)
2 Tiny piece of food (5)
4 Fashioned (6)
5 Intensely painful (12)
6 Flowers with white petals (7)
7 Distinguish between (13)
8 Disorganised person (12)
14 A general proposition (7)
16 Moved repeatedly from side to side (6)
19 Alleviate (5)

No 33

Across

1 Physical wound (6)
7 Structure giving lift in flight (8)
8 Beam of light (3)
9 Soft felt hat (6)
10 Decorated a cake (4)
11 Frozen fruit juice on a stick (5)
13 Least attractive (7)
15 Social reject (7)
17 Expressing emotions (of poetry) (5)
21 Spiritual teacher (4)
22 Enrol in the armed services (6)
23 Snake-like fish (3)
24 Disappearing gradually (8)
25 Colour of a lemon (6)

Down

1 Country in the Middle East (6)
2 Feeling great happiness (6)
3 Loutish person (5)
4 Place in order (7)
5 Natural liking for (8)
6 Passenger ships (6)
12 Long scolding speeches (8)
14 Practising self-denial (7)
16 In mint condition (6)
18 Narrate a story once again (6)
19 Immature (6)
20 Mournful poem (5)

No 34

Across

1 Senior monks (6)
5 Insole (anag) (6)
8 Beat with a whip (4)
9 Uncovered; displayed (8)
10 Make amends (5)
11 Electronic retention of data (7)
14 Eg rain or snow (13)
16 Damaging immune response (7)
18 Hurried (5)
20 Cheapest berth on a ship (8)
22 Barrier between rooms (4)
23 Steal; seize suddenly (6)
24 Yellowish-brown pigment (6)

Down

2 Having two sides (9)
3 Derived from living matter (7)
4 Painful or aching (4)
5 Float in the air (8)
6 Ringo ___ : one of the Beatles (5)
7 Lyric poem (3)
12 Deserted settlement (5,4)
13 Engraved inscription (8)
15 Silly talk (7)
17 Happening (5)
19 Large bodies of water (4)
21 Light brown colour (3)

No 35

Across

1 Throws a coin in the air (6)
7 Gratification (8)
8 Purchase (3)
9 Breakfast food (6)
10 Nocturnal birds of prey (4)
11 Removes the lid (5)
13 ___ Monroe: famous actress (7)
15 Fabric (7)
17 Stem of an arrow (5)
21 Encourage in wrongdoing (4)
22 Sewing instrument (6)
23 Away from home (3)
24 Range of hills in N England (8)
25 Exchanged goods (6)

Down

1 Trinidad and ___ : country (6)
2 Obstruct (6)
3 Involuntary muscle contraction (5)
4 Retains (anag) (7)
5 Amaze (8)
6 Type of hat (6)
12 Making ineffective (8)
14 Servile (7)
16 Saturated (6)
18 Ancient (3-3)
19 Sampled (food) (6)
20 Extravagant celebratory meal (5)

No 36

Across

1 Expressing regret (6)
4 Procession (6)
9 Cut of beef (7)
10 Entrust a secret to another (7)
11 Vegetables (5)
12 Pattern (5)
14 Tea container (5)
15 Apathy (5)
17 Wounding remarks (5)
18 Flower-shaped competition award (7)
20 Layer of earth (7)
21 Annoying person (6)
22 Shooting star (6)

Down

1 Toy that is shaken (6)
2 Type of coffee (8)
3 Individual things (5)
5 Useful feature of a place (7)
6 Opposing (4)
7 Surpass (6)
8 Try to predict an outcome (6-5)
13 All people (8)
14 Personal possession (7)
15 Groans (anag) (6)
16 Stableman (6)
17 Religious book (5)
19 Football boot grip (4)

No 37

Across

7 Martial art (4,2)
8 ___ Mauresmo: French former tennis star (6)
9 Protective foot covering (4)
10 Removes errors (8)
11 Massage technique (7)
13 Small seat (5)
15 Sacred song or hymn (5)
16 Antiquated (7)
18 Collected or stored (8)
19 Inspires fear and wonder (4)
21 Knitted pullover (6)
22 Very milky (6)

Down

1 Of like kind (4)
2 Pleasantness (13)
3 Opposite of failure (7)
4 Raced (anag) (5)
5 State of extreme happiness (7,6)
6 Brilliant performers (8)
12 Captives (8)
14 Give rise to (7)
17 Horse carts (5)
20 Trees of the genus Ulmus (4)

No 38

Across

1 Norway lobsters (6)
7 Soft part of a bed (8)
8 Mongrel dog (3)
9 Make beloved (6)
10 Small bottle (4)
11 Work spirit (5)
13 Act of entering (7)
15 Royal attendant (7)
17 Crowbar (5)
21 Fastened with stitches (4)
22 Makes amends for (6)
23 Type of statistical chart (3)
24 Squeezes (8)
25 Annually (6)

Down

1 Farming tool (6)
2 Anew (6)
3 Drive forward (5)
4 Putting away items (7)
5 Journey across (8)
6 Academy Awards (6)
12 Face-to-face conversation (3-2-3)
14 Respire (7)
16 Inhibits; crushes (6)
18 Evening star (6)
19 Make less dense (6)
20 Clamorous (5)

No 39

Across

1 Lazed (5)
4 Incomplete or lacking in detail (7)
7 Small sales stand (5)
8 Ornamental climbing plant (8)
9 Meat and vegetables on a skewer (5)
11 Lawfulness (8)
15 Portable device to keep the rain off (8)
17 Long and imposing poems (5)
19 Standards (8)
20 Work of fiction (5)
21 Helped to happen (7)
22 Bright; cheery (5)

Down

1 Vaccinate (9)
2 Ancestry (7)
3 Fiasco (7)
4 Eject liquid in a jet (6)
5 Biters (anag) (6)
6 Plantain lily (5)
10 Significant change from an established process (9)
12 Reviewers (7)
13 War trumpet (7)
14 Dung beetle (6)
16 Indefinitely large number (6)
18 Feign (3,2)

No 40

Across

1 Manage (4)
3 Public and formal (8)
9 Talk in a rambling way (7)
10 Pointed part of a fork (5)
11 Research place (abbrev) (3)
12 Cook meat in the oven (5)
13 Pond-dwelling amphibians (5)
15 Warning noise from an emergency vehicle (5)
17 Compass point (5)
18 Fall behind (3)
19 Stroll casually (5)
20 One more (7)
21 Boating (8)
22 ___ Blyton: writer (4)

Down

1 Acting to complete a whole (13)
2 Ball of lead (5)
4 Litter of pigs (6)
5 Imitator (12)
6 Set apart (7)
7 Given to thievery (5-8)
8 Firm rebuke (12)
14 Type of respiration (7)
16 Recover (6)
18 Lindsay ___ : US actress (5)

No 41

Across

1 Happen to (someone) (6)
4 Having pimples (6)
9 Pear-shaped fruit (7)
10 Eg Evita (7)
11 Gets less difficult (5)
12 Reversed (5)
14 Greek writer of fables (5)
15 Country in the Himalayas (5)
17 ___ Tuck: friend of Robin Hood (5)
18 Individual character (7)
20 Totals up (7)
21 Rousing from sleep (6)
22 Within this context (6)

Down

1 Made a loud and harsh sound (6)
2 Paper size (8)
3 Dog leashes (5)
5 Exercise for building arm muscles (5-2)
6 Bathroom mineral powder (4)
7 Shouted out very loudly (6)
8 Express sympathy (11)
13 Resolute (8)
14 Distant runner-up in a horse race (4-3)
15 Son of one's brother or sister (6)
16 Jail (6)
17 Not true (5)
19 Unpleasant smell (4)

No 42

Across

1. Material used as a colourant (8)
5. Mocks (4)
8. Abominable snowmen (5)
9. Most favourable (7)
10. Republic in South America (7)
12. Male labourers (7)
14. Respected (7)
16. Marked by prosperity (of a past time) (7)
18. Early 20th century art movement (7)
19. Model; perfect (5)
20. Break away (4)
21. To some degree (8)

Down

1. 24 hour periods (4)
2. Book of the Bible (6)
3. Formal written or spoken statement (9)
4. Rigid; very cold (6)
6. Scented ointment (6)
7. Receiving a wage (8)
11. Serious or unfriendly (9)
12. Over the hill (6-2)
13. Solemn promise (6)
14. Type of living organism (6)
15. Eg rat or squirrel (6)
17. Associate (4)

No 43

Across

1 Curved shapes (4)
3 Composer of a sacred song (8)
9 Gloss (7)
10 Darken (5)
11 Regal (5)
12 Extraordinary occurrence (7)
13 Time of widespread glaciation (3,3)
15 Sporting venues (6)
17 Issue forth (7)
18 ___ Witherspoon: actress (5)
20 Lives (anag) (5)
21 Live together (7)
22 Value greatly (8)
23 Vend (4)

Down

1 Paid announcement (13)
2 Spiced dish (5)
4 Plan of action (6)
5 Scientific research rooms (12)
6 Brought about (7)
7 Unpredictable (13)
8 Binoculars (5,7)
14 Elusive (7)
16 Swordsman (6)
19 Join together; merge (5)

No 44

Across

1 Breathe out (6)
7 Belief taught by a Church (8)
8 Female chicken (3)
9 ___ Tanner: tennis player (6)
10 Semi-precious agate (4)
11 Clod of turf (5)
13 Caused to catch fire (7)
15 Capital of Georgia in the US (7)
17 Uses a keyboard (5)
21 Boyfriend (4)
22 Showered (6)
23 Man's best friend (3)
24 Boring into (8)
25 Willow twigs (6)

Down

1 Reverberated (6)
2 History play by Shakespeare (5,1)
3 Draw or bring out (5)
4 Area of land (7)
5 Precedence in rank (8)
6 Biochemical catalyst (6)
12 Obscurely (8)
14 Faintly illuminated at night (7)
16 Speculative view (6)
18 Oar (6)
19 Raised theatre platforms (6)
20 ___ Mortensen: actor (5)

No 45

Across

1 Burrow that acts as an animal refuge (8)
5 Protective crust over a wound (4)
8 Short choral composition (5)
9 Fail to repay a loan (7)
10 Inspire with love (7)
12 Having patches of colour (7)
14 Woody plant (7)
16 Small bunch of flowers (7)
18 A parent's mother (7)
19 Siren (anag); sticky substance (5)
20 Golf pegs (4)
21 Getting away from (8)

Down

1 Collide with (4)
2 Most recent (6)
3 Young bird (9)
4 Lived with as a guest (6)
6 Robinson ___ : novel (6)
7 Garment worn after a shower (8)
11 Ridge of the Himalayas (9)
12 00:00 on a 24-hour clock (8)
13 Large property with land; holding (6)
14 Go around (6)
15 Dwarfed tree (6)
17 Obstacle (4)

48

No 46

Across

1 Gratitude; acclaim (11)
9 Humming sound (5)
10 Asp (anag) (3)
11 Shout of appreciation (5)
12 Interior (5)
13 Practise for a later performance (8)
16 Vivid (of a colour) (8)
18 Bunches (5)
21 Frustrated and annoyed (3,2)
22 Pen point (3)
23 Great sorrow (5)
24 Solid figure with five faces (11)

Down

2 Ability to understand the feelings of another (7)
3 Piece of furniture (7)
4 Hospital carers (6)
5 Musical speeds (5)
6 Mary-Kate and Ashley ___ : actresses (5)
7 Taking away (11)
8 Visible to the naked eye (11)
14 Ate quickly (7)
15 Decorative style of design (3,4)
17 Sumptuously rich (6)
19 Legend (5)
20 Visual perception (5)

No 47

Across

7 Industrious (8)
8 Upper part of the body (4)
9 A parent's mother (4)
10 Country in Africa (8)
11 Distributing (7)
12 Assumed appearance (5)
15 Burn (5)
17 ___ ball: item used by clairvoyants (7)
20 Word for word (8)
22 Brass musical instrument (4)
23 Sci-fi film with Jeff Bridges (4)
24 Wheeled supermarket vehicles (8)

Down

1 ___ fruit: eg orange or lemon (6)
2 Occurring twice a year (8)
3 Removing frost from a windscreen (2-5)
4 Impress a pattern on (5)
5 Norse god of thunder (4)
6 Horse-drawn vehicles (6)
13 Disturb (8)
14 Deep red colour (7)
16 Small red fruit with a hard stone (6)
18 Church buildings (6)
19 Express one's opinion (5)
21 Strong link (4)

No 48

Across

1. Lofty (4)
3. First public performance (8)
9. Rise into the air (of an aircraft) (4,3)
10. Unabridged (5)
11. Colour or tint (3)
12. Belonging to them (5)
13. Eg Mozart's Don Giovanni (5)
15. Lady (5)
17. Follow the position of (5)
18. Small truck (3)
19. Reside (5)
20. Satisfy a desire (7)
21. Young (8)
22. Group of actors in a show (4)

Down

1. Unenthusiastically (4-9)
2. Blunder (5)
4. Decline to do something; rubbish (6)
5. Hillside (12)
6. Shuns (7)
7. Amusement (13)
8. A grouping of states (12)
14. Flat highland (7)
16. One's environment (6)
18. Longest river in Europe (5)

No 49

Across

1 Trustworthy (11)
9 Seemingly (combining form) (5)
10 Viscous liquid (3)
11 Japanese poem (5)
12 Obtain information from various sources (5)
13 Fragrant toiletries (8)
16 Versions of a book (8)
18 Female servants (5)
21 Christina ___ : Addams Family actress (5)
22 Religious sister (3)
23 Kick out (5)
24 Type of treatment using needles (11)

Down

2 Surpass (7)
3 Agreeably sharp in taste (7)
4 Subtle variation (6)
5 Cake decoration (5)
6 Not tense (5)
7 Accomplishment (11)
8 Stealthy (11)
14 Promising young actress (7)
15 Coupon (7)
17 Visit informally (4,2)
19 Type of chemical bond (5)
20 Engross oneself in (5)

No 50

Across

1 After the beginning of (4)
3 Toughness (8)
9 Transported by hand (7)
10 Faint bird cry (5)
11 Quarrel (3)
12 Change (5)
13 Should (5)
15 Opposite of lower (5)
17 ___ pole: tribal emblem (5)
18 Much ___ About Nothing: play (3)
19 Become very hot (5)
20 Stands about idly (7)
21 Prayer service (8)
22 Circular movement of water (4)

Down

1 Forever honest (13)
2 Chuck (5)
4 Summing together (6)
5 Absolute authority in any sphere (12)
6 Voter (7)
7 In a manner that exceeds what is necessary (13)
8 Type of cloud (12)
14 End result (7)
16 Substance made by flowers (6)
18 In front (5)

No 51

Across

1 Friends (5)
4 Cover or partly cover (7)
7 Innate worth (5)
8 Protector; guardian (8)
9 Performed on stage (5)
11 Compassionate (8)
15 Operate correctly; work (8)
17 Domesticated (5)
19 Stalemate (5-3)
20 Lawful (5)
21 Normally (7)
22 Give up (5)

Down

1 Eg salt or pepper (9)
2 Identifying outfit (7)
3 Template (7)
4 Administrative body (6)
5 Half-conscious state (6)
6 Display freely (5)
10 Respectable; stately (9)
12 Efficiency (7)
13 Retaliatory action (7)
14 Part of the eye (6)
16 Not arranged neatly (6)
18 Assumed name (5)

No 52

Across

1 Musical works (6)
5 Deprived of; lacking (6)
8 Formal dance (4)
9 Cut (8)
10 Plant spike (5)
11 Version of a book (7)
14 Destroying microorganisms (13)
16 Correspondence (7)
18 Latin American dance (5)
20 Type of employment (4-4)
22 Cereal grains (4)
23 Remove an obstruction from a sink (6)
24 Pondering (6)

Down

2 Maybe (9)
3 Japanese army officer (7)
4 Bypass (4)
5 Make valid retrospectively (8)
6 Restore factory settings (5)
7 ___ Rida: American rapper (3)
12 Long-armed ape (5-4)
13 Transporting by hand (8)
15 Rowdy (7)
17 Absolute (5)
19 Group of players; side (4)
21 Bristle-like appendage (3)

No 53

Across

1 Shameless (8)
5 Hired form of transport (4)
9 Tidily kept (5)
10 Horse sound (5)
11 Coded message (10)
14 Although (6)
15 Choice (6)
17 Large kingfisher (10)
20 Floor of a building (5)
21 Small and round and shiny (5)
22 Position adopted for a photo (4)
23 Spotted beetle (8)

Down

1 Writing fluids (4)
2 Short note or reminder (4)
3 Resolvable (12)
4 Slumbers (6)
6 Corrosive precipitation (4,4)
7 Cruel (8)
8 Immeasurably (12)
12 Reverse somersault (8)
13 Pardons (8)
16 Domed roof (6)
18 Country where one finds Bamako (4)
19 Saw; observed (4)

No 54

Across

1 Country in the Middle East (5)
4 Good qualities (7)
7 Hard to please (5)
8 Exultant (8)
9 Receded (5)
11 Burbling (8)
15 Cocktail (8)
17 Expulsion from a country (5)
19 Glue (8)
20 Warning sound (5)
21 Suggested but not stated explicitly (7)
22 Loose stones on a slope (5)

Down

1 Conquer; master (9)
2 Heist (7)
3 In a nimble manner (7)
4 ___ Kay: TV presenter (6)
5 Thick innermost digits (6)
6 Follow on from (5)
10 Portray precisely (9)
12 Containing water (7)
13 Separator (7)
14 Not singular (6)
16 Mixed up or confused (6)
18 Vascular tissue in plants (5)

No 55

Across

1. Challenge (4)
3. Protective garments (8)
9. Offence (7)
10. Dried kernel of the coconut (5)
11. Opposite of a winner (5)
12. Look into (7)
13. Risky (6)
15. Fish with thick lips (6)
17. Become less intense (4,3)
18. Speaks (5)
20. Types (5)
21. Disciple (7)
22. Waterside area (8)
23. State of confusion; disorder (4)

Down

1. Verified for a second time (6-7)
2. Loose outer garments (5)
4. Swerved (6)
5. Convalescence (12)
6. Subatomic particles such as electrons (7)
7. Brazenness (13)
8. Unpredictably (12)
14. Chemical element with atomic number 33 (7)
16. Matter (6)
19. Supple (5)

Across

1 Pygmy chimpanzee (6)
5 Pro (3)
7 Up to the time when (5)
8 People insisting on adherence to traditional rules (7)
9 Delicious (5)
10 Watchful (8)
12 Furthest; extreme (6)
14 ___ Moon: Character in Frasier (6)
17 Decline (8)
18 Ice masses (5)
20 Highest vantage point of a building (7)
21 Creative thoughts (5)
22 Dry (of wine) (3)
23 Acclimatise or accustom (6)

Down

2 Type of optician (7)
3 Groundless (8)
4 Remain (4)
5 Belgian language (7)
6 Use again (7)
7 Exploiting (5)
11 Without shoes (8)
12 Joins together (7)
13 Tuneful (7)
15 Very young infant (7)
16 Calls out like a lion (5)
19 Travelled too quickly (4)

No 57

Across

1. Identical; unchanged (4)
3. Political meetings (8)
9. Sweetened citrus beverage (7)
10. Nursemaid (5)
11. Without equal (12)
13. Lays eggs (6)
15. Ice shoes (6)
17. Creator of film scripts (12)
20. Capital of Vietnam (5)
21. Social gathering of old friends (7)
22. Bouquets (8)
23. ___ Macpherson: Australian supermodel (4)

Down

1. Most foolish (8)
2. Impersonator (5)
4. Stadiums (6)
5. Quarrelsome and uncooperative (12)
6. Sleeveless garment (7)
7. Leguminous plant (4)
8. Enraging worm (anag) (12)
12. Keep at a distance (8)
14. Upward slopes (7)
16. Force; vigour (6)
18. Tremulous sound (5)
19. At what time (4)

No 58

Across

1 Dissatisfied (11)
9 Upper coverings of buildings (5)
10 Small legume (3)
11 Film directed by Ridley Scott (5)
12 Manner of speaking (5)
13 International waters (4,4)
16 Grandiosity of language (8)
18 Wall painting (5)
21 ___ Klum: supermodel (5)
22 One (anag) (3)
23 Civilian dress (5)
24 Urging on (11)

Down

2 Encroach (7)
3 Decorate food (7)
4 System of social perfection (6)
5 Exams (5)
6 Not containing anything (5)
7 Seaside scavenger (11)
8 Curse (11)
14 Engraving (7)
15 Skilled worker (7)
17 Cow (6)
19 Angry dispute (3-2)
20 West Indian dance (5)

No 59

Across

1 Support at the top of a seat (8)
5 Move fast in a straight line (4)
8 ___ Schmidt: film starring Jack Nicholson (5)
9 Pertaining to actuality (7)
10 Country whose capital is Dublin (7)
12 Brushed off the face (of hair) (7)
14 Gasping (7)
16 Nasal opening (7)
18 Perfectly (7)
19 Aimed (anag) (5)
20 Long deep cut (4)
21 Trousers (8)

Down

1 Become healthy again (4)
2 Loves dearly (6)
3 Gun dog (9)
4 Underside of an arch (6)
6 Puma (6)
7 Deceiving (8)
11 Say clearly (9)
12 Incessant (8)
13 Organic compounds (6)
14 Participant in a game (6)
15 Mischievous (6)
17 Mesh (anag) (4)

62

No 60

Across

1 Removes from one's property (6)
5 Yield (6)
8 Leg joint (4)
9 Fictitious (8)
10 Sky-blue colour (5)
11 Chats (7)
14 Rebirth in a new body (13)
16 Stuffing (7)
18 Hang in the air (5)
20 Light afternoon meal (5,3)
22 Insect larva (4)
23 Sloping (of a typeface) (6)
24 Restrain with chains (6)

Down

2 Republic in South America (9)
3 V-shaped line or stripe (7)
4 Unspecified in number (4)
5 Sociable (8)
6 Follows closely (5)
7 North American nation (abbrev) (3)
12 Way of doing something (9)
13 Very attractive (of personality) (8)
15 Mental process or idea (7)
17 Speak in a slow manner (5)
19 Abandoned person (4)
21 Decay (3)

No 61

Across

8 Artificial sweetener (9)
9 Tree (3)
10 Headgear of a monarch (5)
11 Excuse (7)
12 Shrivels up (7)
13 ___ Pound: US poet (4)
17 Unwrap a gift (4)
18 Outfit (7)
22 Female spirit (7)
24 Barack ___ : US President (5)
25 Edible nut (3)
26 Believed (a lie) (9)

Down

1 Food relish (5)
2 Facing (8)
3 Share; portion (7)
4 Door knocker (6)
5 Religious doctrine (5)
6 Uncommon (4)
7 Country house (7)
14 African country (8)
15 European deer (7)
16 Walks leisurely (7)
19 Unidirectional (3-3)
20 Card game (5)
21 Animal that eats bamboo (5)
23 Pen points (4)

No 62

Across

1 ___ in: eat heartily (4)
3 Supreme being (8)
9 Mechanical keyboard (7)
10 Lukewarm (5)
11 Corresponding; proportionate (12)
14 Cutting tool (3)
16 Dwelling (5)
17 Metal container (3)
18 Unnecessarily careful (12)
21 Lump or bump (5)
22 Decorated (7)
23 Reserved in advance (3-5)
24 Walked or stepped (4)

Down

1 Always in a similar role (of an actor) (8)
2 Deep fissure (5)
4 Pasture; meadow (3)
5 Act of seizing something en route (12)
6 Pertaining to the liver (7)
7 Jedi Master in Star Wars films (4)
8 Fellowship (12)
12 Underwater breathing device (5)
13 Unequal (3-5)
15 Ripple on water (7)
19 Possessor (5)
20 Large wading bird (4)
22 Increase in amount (3)

No 63

Across

1 Experienced sailor (3,3)
7 Salve (8)
8 Not me (3)
9 Outsider (6)
10 Matured (4)
11 Suave (5)
13 Steep in; engross (7)
15 Shoulder blade (7)
17 Steps over a fence (5)
21 Group of countries in an alliance (4)
22 With hands on the hips (6)
23 Hair style (3)
24 Person with an appreciation of beauty (8)
25 Not dense (6)

Down

1 Gramophone needle (6)
2 Graduates of an academic institution (6)
3 Silly (5)
4 Study of the body (7)
5 Inherent (8)
6 Reasons (6)
12 Maximum number a stadium can hold (8)
14 Having folds (of a garment) (7)
16 Named (6)
18 Line of equal pressure on a map (6)
19 Fit for consumption (6)
20 Jumps into water (5)

No 64

Across

1 Italian acknowledgement (4)
3 Lacking knowledge (8)
9 A number defining position (7)
10 ___ Way: famous Roman road (5)
11 Our planet (5)
12 Divisions between groups of people (7)
13 Stylish (6)
15 Pencil rubber (6)
17 Religious ceremonies (7)
18 Divided into two (5)
20 Surprise result (5)
21 Capital of Ontario (7)
22 Deep ditches (8)
23 This place (4)

Down

1 Type of surveillance system (6-7)
2 Small venomous snake (5)
4 Waterproof overshoe (6)
5 Unofficially (3,3,6)
6 Aids (7)
7 Hidden store of valuables (8,5)
8 Eager (12)
14 A dancer or singer (7)
16 African fly (6)
19 ___ Els: golfer (5)

No 65

Across

1 Atmospheric phenomenon (6)
7 Pliable sheet of material (8)
8 Eg oxygen (3)
9 Batsman who starts an innings (6)
10 Metal fastener (4)
11 Way in (5)
13 Takes a firm stand (7)
15 Attack (7)
17 Fault; mistake (5)
21 Payment to a landlord (4)
22 Rich cake (6)
23 ___ de Janeiro: Brazilian city (3)
24 Apportioned (8)
25 Mouse sound (6)

Down

1 Mineral of the pyroxene group (6)
2 Place that is frequented for holidays (6)
3 In the company of (5)
4 Have a positive impact (7)
5 Majesty (8)
6 Charge with a crime (6)
12 Response (8)
14 Series of steps between floors of buildings (7)
16 Decorous; proper (6)
18 Mickey ___ : US actor (6)
19 Amend; change (6)
20 Dusts (anag) (5)

No 66

Across

1 Substance used for washing (4)
3 Country in the Indian Ocean (8)
9 Adopt or support a cause (7)
10 Rope with a running noose (5)
11 Colour of grass (5)
12 Exclusion from the workplace (7)
13 Firm or hard sweet (6)
15 Body of running water (6)
17 Envisage (7)
18 Exhibited (5)
20 Inert gas that is present in air (5)
21 Fastest animal on land (7)
22 Distribute (8)
23 Cut with scissors (4)

Down

1 Legerdemain (7,2,4)
2 Fruit (5)
4 ___ Berrabah: member of the Sugababes (6)
5 Type of food shop (12)
6 Rayon fabric (7)
7 Fairness in following the rules (13)
8 Most perfect example of a quality (12)
14 Searches for food (7)
16 Responds to (6)
19 Denise van ___ : English actress (5)

No 67

Across

1 Stride; rate of moving (4)
3 Short account of an incident (8)
9 Temporary camp (7)
10 Memos (5)
11 Contradictory (12)
13 Landowners (6)
15 Spectator (6)
17 Not discernible (12)
20 Protective garment (5)
21 Changed gradually (7)
22 Term for a pet feline (8)
23 Ruse (4)

Down

1 Not privately (8)
2 Relating to a city (5)
4 Sugary flower secretion (6)
5 Placation (12)
6 Effluence (7)
7 Far from difficult (4)
8 Brusque and surly (12)
12 Amicable (8)
14 Entrails (7)
16 ___ Williams: tennis star (6)
18 Tool for marking angles (5)
19 Breathe convulsively (4)

No 68

Across

7 Very brave and courageous (6)
8 Element with atomic number 6 (6)
9 Legal document (4)
10 Cloudy (8)
11 Periodical (7)
13 Capital of France (5)
15 Repository (5)
16 Small house (7)
18 Pertaining to the body (8)
19 Short sleeps (4)
21 Flat-bottomed rowing boat (6)
22 Female parent (6)

Down

1 ___ Moore: US actress (4)
2 Amusement park ride (6,7)
3 Learned person (7)
4 Yearns for (5)
5 Defer action (13)
6 Enhancing; encouraging (8)
12 In the sky (8)
14 SI unit of electric charge (7)
17 Make a search (5)
20 Hunted animal (4)

No 69

Across

1 Diminished (6)
5 Mineral of lead sulphide (6)
8 ___ Fitzgerald: famous jazz singer (4)
9 Beneficiaries of a will (8)
10 Add coal to a fire (5)
11 Impose one's will (7)
14 Coquettishly (13)
16 Delightful (7)
18 Performer (5)
20 Exceptional (8)
22 Undergarment (4)
23 Contemptibly small (6)
24 Ordered arrangements (6)

Down

2 Dismissed as insignificant (9)
3 Device that records the movements of someone (7)
4 Boring (4)
5 Very large (8)
6 Random number game (5)
7 Born (3)
12 Insensitively (9)
13 Legal soundness (8)
15 Reveal (7)
17 Looks slyly (5)
19 Leaf (anag) (4)
21 Perceive with the eyes (3)

No 70

Across

1 More likely than not (4-2)
4 Having only magnitude (of a quantity) (6)
9 Bison (7)
10 Keepsake; reminder (7)
11 Colour lightly (5)
12 Go over again (5)
14 Stage play (5)
15 Doctrine; system of beliefs (5)
17 Postpone (5)
18 Plant with starchy tuberous roots (7)
20 Greek goddess of retribution (7)
21 Decorate with a raised design (6)
22 Stage whispers (6)

Down

1 Planetary paths around the sun (6)
2 Clearly stated (8)
3 Egg-shaped (5)
5 Grotesque monster (7)
6 Area of mown grass (4)
7 Recover; get back (6)
8 Plaintiff (11)
13 Muddled (8)
14 Quantities of medicine (7)
15 Laugh in a harsh way (6)
16 Snack food of potato slices (6)
17 Pantomime ___ : comic characters (5)
19 Stone block (4)

No 71

Across

1 Diving seabirds (4)
3 Soft leather shoe (8)
9 More jolly (7)
10 Smell (5)
11 Cloth for wiping one's nose (12)
14 Sort; kind (3)
16 Outdoor shelters (5)
17 Large salt water body (3)
18 In a carefree manner (12)
21 Fabric with parallel ribs (5)
22 Italian dish (7)
23 Opposite of positive (8)
24 Potato (informal) (4)

Down

1 Comfy seat (8)
2 Donna ___ New York: clothing label (5)
4 Belonging to us (3)
5 Framework for washed garments (7,5)
6 Light periods of rainfall (7)
7 Standard (4)
8 As quickly as possible (7-5)
12 Extent or limit (5)
13 Infancy (8)
15 Done in full awareness (7)
19 Scheme intended to deceive (3-2)
20 Immobilise (4)
22 Increase the running speed of an engine (3)

No 72

Across

1 Ark builder (4)
3 Held out against (8)
9 Concepts (7)
10 Eats like a bird (5)
11 Suggest (5)
12 Wreath of flowers (7)
13 Greek mathematician (6)
15 US state (6)
17 Pasta pockets (7)
18 Special reward (5)
20 Conventions (5)
21 Smoothing clothes (7)
22 Evacuating (8)
23 Stiff paper (4)

Down

1 Absence (13)
2 Singing voices (5)
4 Banner or flag (6)
5 Flaw (12)
6 Musical composition (7)
7 Deprived (13)
8 Luckily (12)
14 Hide (5-2)
16 Sight (6)
19 ___ Dushku: US actress (5)

No 73

Across

8 Cutting; incisive (9)
9 Large primate (3)
10 Erased (5)
11 Superficial wound (7)
12 Tall tower (7)
13 Hew (4)
17 Black ___: Colombian bird (4)
18 Shorten (7)
22 Talk foolishly (7)
24 Dietary roughage (5)
25 Unit of energy (3)
26 Where school lessons take place (9)

Down

1 Cooks slowly in liquid (5)
2 Tyrannical (8)
3 Sped along; skimmed (7)
4 Casual (anag) (6)
5 Long-legged wading bird (5)
6 Tense (4)
7 Possibly (7)
14 Intellectual (8)
15 Tool for cutting metal (7)
16 Spread out (7)
19 Male pub worker (6)
20 Makeshift shelter (5)
21 Microorganisms (5)
23 Ship used by Jason and followers (4)

No 74

Across

1 Every 14 days (11)
9 Lubricated (5)
10 Level golf score (3)
11 Brightly coloured parrot (5)
12 Equip (5)
13 Branch of metaphysics (8)
16 Eg from Tokyo (8)
18 Put into service (5)
21 Dissatisfaction (5)
22 Very cold (3)
23 Love affair (5)
24 Celebrity (11)

Down

2 Quality of lacking transparency (7)
3 Gardening tools (7)
4 Doing nothing (6)
5 Shrub fence (5)
6 Oily organic compound (5)
7 Metabolic equilibrium (11)
8 Set a limit on (4,3,4)
14 Towards the side (7)
15 Tapering flag (7)
17 Border (6)
19 Recipient of money (5)
20 Resay (anag) (5)

No 75

Across

1 State a belief confidently (6)
7 Connection; link (8)
8 Epoch (3)
9 Precious red gems (6)
10 Change (4)
11 Stood up (5)
13 Distance travelled (7)
15 Two lines of verse (7)
17 Puff up (5)
21 Celebrity hero (4)
22 Wildcat (6)
23 Ancient boat (3)
24 Indefatigable (8)
25 Giggle (6)

Down

1 Spiny tree or shrub (6)
2 Dual audio (6)
3 Distinguishing characteristic (5)
4 Flexible (7)
5 Extremely delicate (8)
6 Affecting the emotions (6)
12 Provided (8)
14 Deciphering machine (7)
16 Confer holy orders on (6)
18 Navigational instrument (6)
19 Heart (slang) (6)
20 Wild animal; monster (5)

No 76

Across

7 Come to understand (6)
8 Removed creases from clothes (6)
9 Fail to speak clearly (4)
10 Cricket captains (8)
11 Tenth month of the year (7)
13 Personnel at work (5)
15 Shadow (5)
16 Day of rest and worship (7)
18 Device that reduces vibrations (8)
19 Medium-sized feline (4)
21 Taxonomic groupings (6)
22 Gossip or idle talk (6)

Down

1 Audacity (4)
2 Musical dance co-ordinator (13)
3 Broke into pieces (7)
4 Go to see (5)
5 Ability to get along (13)
6 Modify with new parts (8)
12 Contrasts (8)
14 Orange vegetables (7)
17 Go stealthily or furtively (5)
20 Invalid; void (4)

79

No 77

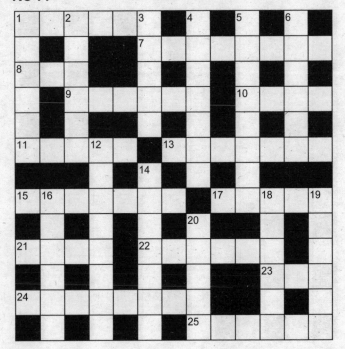

Across

1 Sapper (anag) (6)
7 Something easy or certain (8)
8 Sound of a dove (3)
9 Animal used to catch rabbits (6)
10 Area of a church (4)
11 Piece of information (5)
13 Division of the United Kingdom (7)
15 Receptacle for cigarette residue (7)
17 Saying (5)
21 Thug; oaf (4)
22 Acquired skills (6)
23 Court (3)
24 Discovered (8)
25 Robust (6)

Down

1 Chose (6)
2 Make a financial gain (6)
3 Steep bank or slope (5)
4 Moving on ice (7)
5 Sparkled (8)
6 Ten plus one (6)
12 Unnamed (8)
14 Promotes commercially (7)
16 Cooks in wood chippings (6)
18 Reply (6)
19 Personify (6)
20 Linear measures of three feet (5)

No 78

Across

7 Underprivileged (8)
8 Musical composition (4)
9 Walk awkwardly (4)
10 Beautiful (8)
11 Without interruption (3-4)
12 Intended (5)
15 Home (5)
17 Mends (7)
20 Spherical (8)
22 Official language of Pakistan (4)
23 Circular storage medium (4)
24 Calling (8)

Down

1 Sheep known for its wool (6)
2 Put forward an idea (8)
3 French city (7)
4 Worship; venerate (5)
5 Departed (4)
6 Reddish brown hair colour (6)
13 Appraise (8)
14 Go back on (7)
16 Sea in northern Europe (6)
18 Extremely fashionable; scalding (3-3)
19 Continuing in existence (5)
21 Stream or small river (4)

No 79

Across

1 Plot (8)
5 Speak in a wild way (4)
9 Imitative of the past (5)
10 American R&B singer (5)
11 Athletics contest (10)
14 Andre ___ : tennis player (6)
15 Putting lawns in golf (6)
17 Belonging to the past (10)
20 Small room used as a steam bath (5)
21 Messenger (5)
22 Expel; drive out (4)
23 Popular type of office layout (4-4)

Down

1 Wine bottle closure (4)
2 Write down (4)
3 Opposite of amateur (12)
4 Revolve (6)
6 Greek hero of the Trojan War (8)
7 Sharpness (of taste) (8)
8 Underground (12)
12 Exaggerated masculinity (8)
13 Sues arms (anag) (8)
16 Accident (6)
18 Egg-shaped (4)
19 ___ Giggs: football star (4)

No 80

Across

1 Insubordinate (11)
9 Leader or ruler (5)
10 Frying pan (3)
11 Word of farewell (5)
12 Ice hockey buildings (5)
13 More attractive (8)
16 Large snake (8)
18 Tall structure on a castle (5)
21 Call forth or cause (5)
22 Eccentric (3)
23 ___ Streep: Mamma Mia! actress (5)
24 Leader in a race (5,6)

Down

2 Catches fire (7)
3 Conceals something from view (7)
4 A political exile (6)
5 Conclude (5)
6 Certain to fail (2-3)
7 Distribute again (11)
8 Very tall buildings (11)
14 Formation of troops (7)
15 Type of bill (7)
17 Closer (6)
19 Less narrow (5)
20 Manor (anag) (5)

83

No 81

Across

1 Spoof (6)
5 Deer (3)
7 Divide by cutting (5)
8 Took along (7)
9 Jumps (5)
10 Pear-shaped fruits (8)
12 Moved steadily (of a river) (6)
14 Stretch prior to exercise (4-2)
17 Highly desirable food item (8)
18 Taut (5)
20 Cutting back a tree (7)
21 Dressed to the ___ : elaborately clothed (5)
22 Excessively (3)
23 Tropical fruit (6)

Down

2 Act of turning up (7)
3 In poor condition (3-5)
4 Morally wicked (4)
5 Printed mistake (7)
6 Affinity (7)
7 Got to one's feet (5)
11 A Roman emperor (8)
12 Most healthy (7)
13 Aromatic herb (7)
15 Mysterious (7)
16 Derives the benefits (5)
19 Army vehicle (4)

No 82

Across

1 Rescue (4)
3 Refer to famous people one knows (4-4)
9 Laid open to view (7)
10 Chaplain in the armed services (5)
11 Sea duck (5)
12 Annoying pain (7)
13 Scuffle (6)
15 Among (6)
17 Farm implements (7)
18 Tortilla topped with cheese (5)
20 Comedian (5)
21 Pastures (7)
22 Publican (8)
23 Catch sight of (4)

Down

1 Lacking originality (13)
2 Lacking interest (5)
4 Mixes up or confuses (6)
5 Based on untested ideas (12)
6 Decreased (7)
7 Affectedly (13)
8 Relating to horoscopes (12)
14 The ___ : book by Raymond Briggs (7)
16 Moires (anag) (6)
19 Loses heat (5)

No 83

Across

1 Having a firm basis in reality (11)
9 Stylishness and originality (5)
10 High ball in tennis (3)
11 Length of interlaced hair (5)
12 Musical note (5)
13 Sonorous (8)
16 Commotion (8)
18 Of the nose (5)
21 Relinquish (5)
22 Rocky peak (3)
23 Eighth Greek letter (5)
24 Act of staying away from work (11)

Down

2 Elevate (7)
3 Sorting through (7)
4 River in South America (6)
5 Palpitate (5)
6 One-way flow structure (5)
7 Chance to do something (11)
8 Room used by astronomers (11)
14 Uppermost layer of something (7)
15 Gourds with green skin (7)
17 Do the same thing again (6)
19 Small woody plant (5)
20 Espresso coffee and steamed milk (5)

No 84

Across

1 Wrong in judgement (8)
5 Dutch cheese (4)
9 Locomotive (5)
10 Attendant upon God (5)
11 Arrangement of events in time order (10)
14 Songbird (6)
15 Where one watches films (6)
17 Animal thymus gland eaten as food (10)
20 Piece of code to automate a task (5)
21 Inactive (5)
22 Reckless; hasty (4)
23 Pristine (5-3)

Down

1 Silent (4)
2 Fly high (4)
3 Complete destruction (12)
4 Implant deeply (6)
6 Well-meaning but interfering person (2-6)
7 Our galaxy (5,3)
8 Declaration of sainthood (12)
12 User; purchaser (8)
13 Permits (8)
16 Intense feeling of love (6)
18 Restrain (4)
19 Cook slowly in liquid (4)

No 85

Across

1 Written laws (8)
5 Opposite of pass (4)
8 About (5)
9 Remove or take out (7)
10 Perceived by touch (7)
12 Swears (7)
14 On the sheltered side (7)
16 Twirl (7)
18 Giggles (7)
19 Spacious (5)
20 Sprints (4)
21 Increase (8)

Down

1 Draw into the mouth using a straw (4)
2 Afloat (6)
3 Not embarrassed (9)
4 Votes into office (6)
6 Middle Eastern language (6)
7 Made untidy with rubbish (8)
11 Type of restaurant (9)
12 Troublemaker (8)
13 Heed (6)
14 Glasses contain these (6)
15 Long-haired variety of cat (6)
17 Extravagant publicity (4)

Across

1 Wine container (4)
3 Disordered state of mind (8)
9 Goals (7)
10 Book leaves (5)
11 Established custom (5)
12 Perfect happiness (7)
13 Free from ostentation (6)
15 Capital of Austria (6)
17 Highest singing voice (7)
18 Fill with high spirits (5)
20 Isolated (5)
21 Slope (7)
22 Sketching out (8)
23 Liability (4)

Down

1 Reach the required standard (3,3,7)
2 Cleanse by rubbing (5)
4 Relaxing (6)
5 Impudence (12)
6 Firmly fix in a person (7)
7 Ineptitude in running a business (13)
8 Second part of the Bible (3,9)
14 Certificate (7)
16 Movement (6)
19 Live by (5)

No 87

Across

7 Phone an unknown person (4,4)
8 Long grass (4)
9 Computer virus (4)
10 Actor (8)
11 Subdivision (7)
12 Deliberate; cogitate (5)
15 Rush (5)
17 Last beyond (7)
20 International negotiator (8)
22 Facial disguise (4)
23 Afresh (4)
24 Melanins (anag) (8)

Down

1 Wolflike wild dog (6)
2 Mileage tracker (8)
3 Warning (7)
4 Moves through the air (5)
5 Grasp tightly (4)
6 Keep hold of (6)
13 Flag position to indicate mourning (4-4)
14 Driving out (7)
16 Workers' groups (6)
18 Concerned with sight (6)
19 Petite (5)
21 Opposite of highs (4)

No 88

Across

1 Top boat in a fleet (8)
5 Unpleasant smell (4)
8 Polish monetary unit (5)
9 Important church (7)
10 Type of monkey (7)
12 Print anew (7)
14 Dilemma (7)
16 Assistant; follower (7)
18 Ardent (7)
19 Trees (anag) (5)
20 Exercise venues (4)
21 Tardiness (8)

Down

1 Frizzy mass of hair (4)
2 Long-legged rodent (6)
3 Elegantly (9)
4 Prisoner (6)
6 Semiaquatic fish eating mammals (6)
7 Popular flowering plant (8)
11 Egg-laying mammal (9)
12 Narrating (8)
13 Opposite of top (6)
14 Former Spanish currency (6)
15 Surface coating (6)
17 Materials from which metals are extracted (4)

No 89

Across

1 Not so important (6)
5 Robberies (6)
8 Edible fruit (4)
9 Frustrated (8)
10 Instruct (5)
11 Ardently; keenly (7)
14 Amazingly (13)
16 Supplanted (7)
18 Pinch; squeeze (5)
20 Ascot cat (anag) (8)
22 Female servant (4)
23 Hard to digest (of food) (6)
24 Not disposed to cheating (6)

Down

2 Morning break (informal) (9)
3 Hot wind blowing from North Africa (7)
4 Rank (4)
5 Trails alongside canals (8)
6 Strange and mysterious (5)
7 Definite article (3)
12 Songs for babies (9)
13 Ability to read (8)
15 Male TV announcers (7)
17 Competed in a speed contest (5)
19 Scottish lake (4)
21 Blue ___ : bird (3)

No 90

Across

1 Spanish title for a married woman (6)
7 Footballers whose role is to score (8)
8 Ram (anag) (3)
9 Majestic (6)
10 Repast (4)
11 Reddish (5)
13 Cargo (7)
15 Involve in conflict (7)
17 White waterbird (5)
21 Soon; shortly (4)
22 Dry and brittle (of food) (6)
23 Cut grass (3)
24 Remove from action (8)
25 Small carnivorous mammal (6)

Down

1 Boil gently (6)
2 Cared for (6)
3 Put a question to (5)
4 Act of making payments to gain favour (7)
5 Reading quickly (8)
6 Raise for discussion (6)
12 Mad (8)
14 Lap of a track (7)
16 Praying ___ : insect (6)
18 Poems; sounds alike (6)
19 Gardening tool (6)
20 Tough fibrous tissue (5)

No 91

Across

1 ___ Major: the Great Bear (4)
3 Restore confidence to (8)
9 Evaluating competition entries (7)
10 Ethical (5)
11 Mexican plant fibre (5)
12 Speaking (7)
13 Situated within a building (6)
15 Imperative (6)
17 Endanger (7)
18 Colossus (5)
20 Short high-pitched tone (5)
21 Mediocre (7)
22 Quotidian (8)
23 Liquefy (4)

Down

1 Indefensible (13)
2 Soft drinks (US) (5)
4 Fourscore (6)
5 Areas of commonality (12)
6 Country whose capital is Kiev (7)
7 The ___ : intellectual movement (13)
8 List of books referred to (12)
14 Use up; exhaust (7)
16 Mammal related to the llama (6)
19 Historic nobleman (5)

Across

1 Agreeing with a request (11)
9 Pertaining to the sun (5)
10 Performed an action (3)
11 Indian rice dish (5)
12 Indifferent to emotions (5)
13 People who lived in times long past (8)
16 Squid (8)
18 Hazy (5)
21 Pile of stones as a landmark (5)
22 Zero (3)
23 Excuse of any kind (5)
24 Generous (11)

Down

2 Part of a horse's leg (7)
3 Provider of financial cover (7)
4 A cereal (6)
5 Conditions (5)
6 Record on tape (5)
7 Act of making peace (11)
8 Serving to enlighten; instructive (11)
14 Element needed by the body (7)
15 Type of deer (7)
17 Mete out (6)
19 Latin American dance (5)
20 Long for (5)

No 93

Across

1 Bone of the forearm (4)
3 Sewage discharged into water (8)
9 Turns upside down (7)
10 Confronts; deals with (5)
11 Connection; link (3-2)
12 Entrap (7)
13 Song words (6)
15 Exist permanently in (6)
17 Young children (7)
18 Underside of a projecting roof (5)
20 Rub out (5)
21 Be given (7)
22 Medicine (8)
23 Jumbo ___ : airliners (4)

Down

1 Not clever (13)
2 Flaring stars (5)
4 Attach firmly (6)
5 Jail term without end (4,8)
6 Valence (anag) (7)
7 Blandness (13)
8 Exceptional (12)
14 Desist from (7)
16 Loan shark (6)
19 Verbalise (5)

No 94

Across

7 Bowed to royalty (8)
8 Bitter-tasting substance (4)
9 Change direction suddenly (4)
10 Loftiness (8)
11 Part of an orchestra (7)
12 Variety of coffee (5)
15 Awards (informal) (5)
17 Platform projecting from a wall (7)
20 Sanctions (8)
22 Places in position (4)
23 Skin irritation (4)
24 One who creates new products (8)

Down

1 Glowing with light (6)
2 Rousing (8)
3 Year in which wine was produced (7)
4 Mix up; confuse (5)
5 Small mountain lake (4)
6 Brandy distilled from cherries (6)
13 Resident (8)
14 Huge (7)
16 Elaborately adorned (6)
18 Country (6)
19 Up and about (5)
21 Where darts players throw from (4)

No 95

Across

1. Adequate in number (11)
9. Daniel ___ : James Bond actor (5)
10. Compete for (3)
11. Pile (5)
12. Noble gas (5)
13. Conclusive examination (4,4)
16. Changing (8)
18. Embarrass (5)
21. Momentary oversight (5)
22. Gratuity (3)
23. Bring together (5)
24. Act of publishing in several places (11)

Down

2. Unpredictable (7)
3. Pouches (7)
4. Ascots (anag) (6)
5. Tool for boring holes (5)
6. Really angry (5)
7. Eating establishments (11)
8. Unintelligible (11)
14. Someone who studies data (7)
15. River of SE Africa (7)
17. Lunatic (6)
19. Sufficiently (5)
20. Dog (5)

No 96

Across

1 Allotted quantity (5)
4 Fall back (7)
7 Savoury meat jelly (5)
8 Pasta in the form of narrow ribbons (8)
9 Take part in combat (5)
11 Break (8)
15 Period when a machine is out of action (8)
17 Torn apart (5)
19 Final teenage year (8)
20 Unpleasant facial expression (5)
21 Petitions to God (7)
22 Student (5)

Down

1 Match to get into a tournament (9)
2 Relating to Oxford (7)
3 Motivate (7)
4 ___ bean: vegetable (6)
5 Attack (6)
6 Metal worker (5)
10 Occurring every three years (9)
12 Surround entirely (7)
13 Jumbled (5-2)
14 Margin of safety (6)
16 States as one's opinion (6)
18 Bring on oneself (5)

No 97

Across

7 Energy (8)
8 Makes a mistake (4)
9 Solid (4)
10 Letters of a language (8)
11 Novice driver (7)
12 Employed (5)
15 Part of a church tower (5)
17 Type of humour (7)
20 Uncovered (of a building) (8)
22 Letters and parcels generally (4)
23 Shoe with a wooden sole (4)
24 Skin care product (8)

Down

1 Conclusion (6)
2 Person walking aimlessly (8)
3 Widens (7)
4 Insect larva (5)
5 Second Greek letter (4)
6 Mourn the loss of (6)
13 Arriving (8)
14 Cricket hitters (7)
16 Ill (6)
18 Cut up (6)
19 Long wooden seat (5)
21 Soft pear-shaped fruits (4)

No 98

Across

1 Alter or move slightly (6)
5 Pull at (3)
7 Christmas show (abbrev) (5)
8 Intimidate (7)
9 Permit (5)
10 Tempting (8)
12 Publishes (6)
14 Ancient Persian king (6)
17 Wrongdoings (8)
18 Town ___ : official who makes public announcements (5)
20 Pencil rubbers (7)
21 Printed insert supplied with a CD (5)
22 Touch gently (3)
23 Person after whom a discovery is named (6)

Down

2 Prophet (7)
3 Shortage (8)
4 ___ Kournikova: former tennis star (4)
5 Chest for implements (7)
6 Scowls (7)
7 Fractional monetary unit (5)
11 Car light (8)
12 Brawl (5-2)
13 Restrain (7)
15 Old (7)
16 Uncertain; risky (5)
19 Actor's part in a film (4)

No 99

Across

1 Steals from (4)
3 Particular event (8)
9 Slide (7)
10 Become ready to eat (of fruit) (5)
11 Clarity (12)
14 Eg pecan or cashew (3)
16 Ethos (anag) (5)
17 Organ of sight (3)
18 Unpleasant (12)
21 ___ Midler: American comedienne (5)
22 Extreme nervousness (7)
23 ___ hour: the latest possible moment (8)
24 Lyric poems (4)

Down

1 Permanent inhabitant (8)
2 Starts to bubble (of liquid) (5)
4 Vehicle (3)
5 Agreements; plans (12)
6 Dead end (7)
7 Not any of (4)
8 24th December (9,3)
12 Church singers (5)
13 Turns around (8)
15 Spiky weed (7)
19 Mix smoothly (5)
20 Having inherent ability (4)
22 Note down (3)

No 100

Across

7 Obsession (8)
8 Thin strip of wood (4)
9 Very short skirt or dress (4)
10 Mountaineers (8)
11 Advertising placards (7)
12 Frozen dew (5)
15 Customary (5)
17 Listless (7)
20 Wave or flourish a weapon (8)
22 Dominion (4)
23 Flirtatious girl (4)
24 Immediately after this (8)

Down

1 Sandstone constituent (6)
2 Large Spanish estate (8)
3 Perceive with the senses (7)
4 Undo a knot (5)
5 Fluent but shallow (of words) (4)
6 Keeps (6)
13 Extremely thorough (8)
14 Groups together (7)
16 Narrow passage of water (6)
18 Ice buildings (6)
19 Dubious (5)
21 Coming immediately after (4)

No 101

Across

1 Expanse of grass (5)
4 Sleeveless cloaks (5)
10 Chain of flowers (7)
11 Triangular river mouth (5)
12 US state (4)
13 Professional comedian (8)
16 Type of canoe (6)
17 Arrive (4,2)
20 Discrete; distinct (8)
21 At a distance (4)
23 Expect; think that (5)
25 Infective agents (7)
26 Hangs (anag) (5)
27 Snake toxin (5)

Down

2 Doing the dishes (7-2)
3 Eurasian crow (4)
5 Item of additional book matter (8)
6 Measure of length (3)
7 Have sufficient money to pay for (6)
8 Cancel (5)
9 Young deer (4)
14 Public declaration of policy (9)
15 Arguments (8)
18 Pedant (6)
19 ___ Coogan: English comedian (5)
20 Drive away (4)
22 At liberty (4)
24 Charged particle (3)

No 102

Across

1 Garment for the foot (4)
3 Large celebration (8)
9 More fortunate (7)
10 Andrew Lloyd Webber musical (5)
11 Pay out money (5)
12 Vague understanding; hint (7)
13 Tall castle structures (6)
15 Follow-up drink (6)
17 Eg Jones or Smith (7)
18 Not concealed (5)
20 Small body of land (5)
21 Contradicted; neutralised (7)
22 Boldly (8)
23 Solely (4)

Down

1 Complacent and happy with oneself (4-9)
2 Ride a bike (5)
4 Nimble (6)
5 Productive insight (12)
6 Dried grapes (7)
7 In an inflated manner (13)
8 School for young children (12)
14 Small songbird; singer (7)
16 Occurring in spring (6)
19 ___ John: Rocket Man singer (5)

No 103

Across

1 Least polite (6)
4 Stagnation or inactivity (6)
9 Bloodsucking creature (7)
10 Fishing boat (7)
11 Ordered arrangement (5)
12 ___ owl: common Eurasian owl (5)
14 Slopes (5)
15 With speed (5)
17 Person who goes on long walks (5)
18 Fish tanks (7)
20 Day of the week (7)
21 Gas we breathe (6)
22 Subatomic particle such as a nucleon (6)

Down

1 Expose (6)
2 Light brown cane sugar (8)
3 Piquant (5)
5 Occupants of a rented property (7)
6 Earth (4)
7 Casual but stylish (of clothing) (6)
8 Having definite limits (11)
13 Evilly (8)
14 Go back over again (7)
15 In slow time (of music) (6)
16 Stick of coloured wax (6)
17 Doglike mammal (5)
19 Unattractive (4)

No 104

Across

1 Annoy (4)
3 Announce publicly (8)
9 Wealthy businesspeople (7)
10 What an author writes (5)
11 Ancient (3)
12 Made a mistake (5)
13 Consumer of food (5)
15 Country in southern Asia (5)
17 Circle a planet (5)
18 23rd Greek letter (3)
19 Adult insect stage (5)
20 Inactive (7)
21 Finance department (8)
22 Beloved; expensive (4)

Down

1 Weather forecaster (13)
2 Decaf (anag) (5)
4 Oppose (6)
5 Room attached to a house (12)
6 Commercials (7)
7 Manage badly (13)
8 Contests (12)
14 Oscillate (7)
16 Flakes of skin in an animal's fur (6)
18 Stage (5)

No 105

Across

7 Short-sightedness (6)
8 Where bees are kept (6)
9 Russian sovereign (4)
10 Royal domains (8)
11 Sprinting (7)
13 Representative (5)
15 Hurts (5)
16 Friendly (7)
18 Disease caused by a lack of thiamine (8)
19 Recess (4)
21 Kicked or hit hard (6)
22 Cream pastry (6)

Down

1 Hair colourants (4)
2 Understandable (13)
3 Woofing (7)
4 Pale or dim (5)
5 Capable of being decomposed (13)
6 Felon (8)
12 Relating to education and scholarship (8)
14 Policeman or policewoman (7)
17 Studies a subject at university (5)
20 Travel on water (4)

Across

1 Very small African parrot (8)
5 Walk with heavy steps (4)
9 Game of chance (5)
10 Bits of meat of low value (5)
11 From beginning to end (10)
14 Mistakes (6)
15 Lively Spanish dance (6)
17 Desirable features (10)
20 Spiritual nourishment (5)
21 Confound (5)
22 Stage of twilight (4)
23 Intelligentsia (8)

Down

1 Part of the ear (4)
2 Opening for air; outlet (4)
3 Male relation by marriage (7-2-3)
4 Calculate (6)
6 Remaining; surplus (8)
7 Reduction in strength (8)
8 Bring together into a mass (12)
12 Made still (8)
13 Precludes (8)
16 US state of islands (6)
18 Spanish sparkling wine (4)
19 Legendary creature (4)

Across

1. ___ Daly: TV presenter (4)
3. In good spirits (8)
9. Lacking depth (7)
10. Brace (5)
11. Orcas (6,6)
14. Grandmother (3)
16. Gold block (5)
17. In favour of (3)
18. Dimly; not clearly (12)
21. Strong lightweight wood (5)
22. Large bag (7)
23. Anxious uncertainty (8)
24. Comedy sketch (4)

Down

1. Capital of Uzbekistan (8)
2. Gastropod (5)
4. In what way (3)
5. Bewitchingly (12)
6. Sudden outburst of something (5-2)
7. Circuits of a racetrack (4)
8. Unlawful (12)
12. Isle of ___ : island near Southampton (5)
13. Knowing many languages (8)
15. Render utterly perplexed (7)
19. Trail (5)
20. Recedes (4)
22. Belonging to him (3)

No 108

Across

7 Gambling house (6)
8 Belonging to them (6)
9 Agitate (4)
10 Speak unfavourably about (3-5)
11 Jumpers (7)
13 English racecourse (5)
15 Climbing shrubs (5)
16 Praise; exalt (7)
18 Squashes (8)
19 ___ Amos: US singer-songwriter (4)
21 Coniferous tree (6)
22 Season before Christmas (6)

Down

1 Endure (4)
2 Rude (13)
3 Cattle herders (US) (7)
4 Composition for a solo instrument (5)
5 Serving to show (13)
6 Vehicle that is beyond repair (5-3)
12 Wrapper for a letter (8)
14 Ionised gases (7)
17 State of nervous excitement; high temperature (5)
20 Step on a ladder (4)

No 109

Across

1 Chess piece (6)
4 Exhausts (6)
9 Ditherer (7)
10 Something left over (7)
11 Drives out from a place (5)
12 Choose to do something (5)
14 Titles (5)
15 Country in SE Asia (5)
17 Small insect (5)
18 Severely damaged (7)
20 Ennoble (7)
21 Flood (6)
22 Bumps into (6)

Down

1 Show servile deference (6)
2 Person who puts money into something (8)
3 Hard outgrowths on animals (5)
5 Swims like a dog (7)
6 ___ Campbell: actress (4)
7 Group of six (6)
8 Tolerant in one's views (5-6)
13 Definite and clear (8)
14 Pestering constantly (7)
15 Prohibited (6)
16 Venomous snakes (6)
17 ___ du Beke: ballroom dancer (5)
19 Meat from a calf (4)

No 110

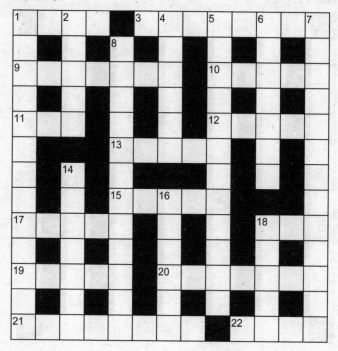

Across

1 Knuckle of pork (4)
3 Clothing that covers the legs (8)
9 Requiring (7)
10 Nice-smelling colourless volatile liquid (5)
11 Strong spirit (3)
12 Small flexible bag (5)
13 Frame for holding an artist's work (5)
15 Eccentric (5)
17 Get by begging (5)
18 Performance by a musician (3)
19 Confusion (3-2)
20 Canopies (7)
21 Channels of the nose (8)
22 Seabird (4)

Down

1 British actress in Goldfinger (5,8)
2 Dairy product (5)
4 Legal entitlements (6)
5 Joblessness (12)
6 Wear out completely (7)
7 The Duchess of York (5,8)
8 Specialist cricketing position (12)
14 Alphabetical lists (7)
16 Soup flavour (6)
18 Variety or kind (5)

No 111

Across

1 Perilously (11)
9 Assembly (5)
10 Chemical element (3)
11 Loud resonant noise (5)
12 Bond or connection (5)
13 An indirect implication (8)
16 Clock timing device (8)
18 Avoided by social custom (5)
21 Small firework (5)
22 Possess (3)
23 Tests (5)
24 Acting out a part (4,7)

Down

2 Reaches (7)
3 Laughs (7)
4 Firmly established (6)
5 Unfasten (5)
6 Milky fluid found in some plants (5)
7 Preference; liking (11)
8 Incalculable (11)
14 A long wandering journey (7)
15 Egg white (7)
17 Impose or require (6)
19 Stringed instrument (5)
20 Corpulent (5)

Across

1 Woes; problems (4)
3 Impetus (8)
9 Distress (7)
10 Shoe ties (5)
11 Respond to (5)
12 Knot or coil of hair (7)
13 Frightens; startles (6)
15 ___ Keys: US singer (6)
17 Freezing (3-4)
18 Punctuation mark (5)
20 Metal spikes (5)
21 Chanted (7)
22 A period of 366 days (4,4)
23 Source of fibre (4)

Down

1 Between countries (13)
2 ___ Lewis: British singer (5)
4 From that place (6)
5 A large number (12)
6 Terse (7)
7 Thelma & Louise actress (5,8)
8 In a sparing manner (12)
14 United States (7)
16 ___ Currie: former politician (6)
19 Underground worker (5)

No 113

Across

7 Small cave (6)
8 Makes more attractive (6)
9 Long poem (4)
10 People who construct things (8)
11 Restrict (7)
13 Gets through merit (5)
15 Gain knowledge (5)
16 Distinct sentence parts (7)
18 20th-century art movement (8)
19 Every (4)
21 Repositories (6)
22 Remove goods from a van (6)

Down

1 Snare (4)
2 Black Eyed Peas star (5,8)
3 Up-and-down movement (7)
4 Sudden fear (5)
5 Amiably (4-9)
6 Doorway (8)
12 Exploits to excess (8)
14 Loud outcry (7)
17 ___ Elliott: US singer (5)
20 Applaud (4)

No 114

Across

1 Skin on top of the head (5)
4 Rushes along; skims (5)
10 Squeeze into a compact mass (7)
11 Snake (5)
12 Gelatinous substance (4)
13 Distinguishing mark (8)
16 Dishes of leafy greens (6)
17 Listener (6)
20 Reasoning logically (8)
21 Pavement edge (4)
23 Expel (5)
25 Film starring Jim Carrey (3,4)
26 Overly showy (5)
27 Late (5)

Down

2 Cut short (9)
3 Give temporarily (4)
5 Joins together (8)
6 Water barrier (3)
7 Pieces of writing (6)
8 Collision; shift (5)
9 ___ Del Rey: singer (4)
14 Nanny (9)
15 Taught (8)
18 Reprimand (6)
19 Midges (5)
20 Ruminant mammal (4)
22 Catherine ___ Jones:
   Welsh actress (4)
24 Distinct historical period (3)

No 115

Across

1 Occupations (4)
3 Not genuine (8)
9 Competitors in a sprint (7)
10 Quantitative relation between two amounts (5)
11 Tell off (5)
12 Obvious (7)
13 Burrowing long-eared mammal (6)
15 Former British coin (6)
17 Wanderer (7)
18 Bird droppings used as fertiliser (5)
20 Prod with one's elbow (5)
21 Thin paper products used for wiping (7)
22 Publicity (8)
23 Wet with condensation (4)

Down

1 Philosophy of law (13)
2 Small drum (5)
4 Bother (6)
5 Heart specialist (12)
6 Last longer than (7)
7 Impulsively (13)
8 Presiding female officer of a school (12)
14 Form or accumulate steadily (5-2)
16 Author (6)
19 Entertain (5)

Across

1 Fill to capacity; stuff (4)
3 Prompt (8)
9 Creatures (7)
10 Competes in a speed contest (5)
11 In accordance with general custom (12)
13 Having a rough surface (of terrain) (6)
15 Document fastener (6)
17 Careful management of the environment (12)
20 Unit of weight (5)
21 Tidal wave (7)
22 Formidable (8)
23 Stringed instrument (4)

Down

1 Office attached to an embassy (8)
2 Pertaining to birds (5)
4 Surprise results (6)
5 Type of cloud (12)
6 Unfasten (7)
7 Opposite of win (4)
8 Failure to act with prudence (12)
12 During the intervening period (8)
14 Adult (5-2)
16 Positively charged atomic particle (6)
18 Where one finds Rome (5)
19 Large desert in Asia (4)

No 117

Across

7 Act of removal (8)
8 Among (4)
9 Be suspended (4)
10 Assuages (8)
11 Small dog (7)
12 Awake (5)
15 Large black birds (5)
17 Varied (7)
20 Subdue; vanquish (8)
22 Electrically charged particles (4)
23 Protest march (abbrev) (4)
24 Where one parks the car (8)

Down

1 Slander (6)
2 Fence formed by bushes (8)
3 Penetrated (7)
4 Went down on one knee (5)
5 Valley (4)
6 Pieces of tough fibrous tissue (6)
13 Short joke (3-5)
14 Zeppelin (7)
16 Paths (6)
18 Open type of footwear (6)
19 Gives temporarily (5)
21 Small body of water (4)

No 118

Across

1 Ancient Persian governor (6)
4 Feature (6)
9 High spirits (7)
10 Drowses (anag) (7)
11 Garden tools (5)
12 Wading birds (5)
14 Epic poem ascribed to Homer (5)
15 Held on to something tightly (5)
17 Extreme displeasure (5)
18 Conceited dandy (7)
20 Living in another's home (7)
21 Poem of fourteen lines (6)
22 US state (6)

Down

1 Britney ___ : singer (6)
2 Expression of gratitude (5,3)
3 Wrong (5)
5 Person who looks after the passengers on a ship (7)
6 Simplicity (4)
7 Long essay or dissertation (6)
8 Not wanted (11)
13 Dwindling (8)
14 Dishonourable (7)
15 Rides a bike (6)
16 Fire-breathing monster (6)
17 Tree of the birch family (5)
19 Superhero film based on comic characters (1-3)

No 119

Across

1. Rivulet (5)
4. Humming (5)
10. Arrogant person (7)
11. Reddish-brown colour (5)
12. Suppress (4)
13. Copied (8)
16. Roofing material made of straw (6)
17. Jewels formed in oyster shells (6)
20. One of the Channel Islands (8)
21. Rail (anag) (4)
23. Self-evident truth (5)
25. Study of animals (7)
26. Light meal (5)
27. Takes part in a game (5)

Down

2. Become evident again (9)
3. Gemstone (4)
5. Infatuated (8)
6. Hit forcibly (3)
7. Variety of grape (6)
8. Plant stalks (5)
9. Stick used by a magician (4)
14. Region (9)
15. Using the minimum necessary (8)
18. Flower arrangements (6)
19. ___-soprano: singing voice (5)
20. Bite at persistently (4)
22. Girl's toy (4)
24. Pub (3)

No 120

Across

1 Type of postage stamp (6-5)
9 Arm joint (5)
10 Herb (3)
11 ___ Federer: tennis star (5)
12 Type of leather (5)
13 One who travels to work regularly (8)
16 Open resistance (8)
18 Precious gem (5)
21 Egg-shaped solid (5)
22 Fishing stick (3)
23 Words that identify things (5)
24 Mean (5-6)

Down

2 Final stage of a process (7)
3 Burdensome (7)
4 Take a casual interest in (6)
5 Areas of mown grass (5)
6 Bout of extravagant shopping (5)
7 Science of farming (11)
8 Calm and sensible (5-6)
14 Type of cell division (7)
15 Swell with fluid (7)
17 Surround (6)
19 Foot-operated lever (5)
20 Areas; sectors (5)

No 121

Across

1 Meeting plan (6)
7 Propelling the body through water (8)
8 Cooking appliance (3)
9 Pantry (6)
10 Tiny amount (4)
11 Third Greek letter (5)
13 ___ Hudgens: High School Musical star (7)
15 Decorative framework (7)
17 Violent atmospheric disturbance (5)
21 Cat sound (4)
22 Sayings (6)
23 Seventh Greek letter (3)
24 Temple dedicated to all the gods (8)
25 Vitreous (6)

Down

1 Hurting (6)
2 Symbol or representation (6)
3 Apart from (5)
4 Active during the day (7)
5 Impending (8)
6 Joins together (6)
12 Opposite of majority (8)
14 Run with light steps (7)
16 Of the eye (6)
18 Be preoccupied with something (6)
19 Disease of the body (6)
20 Chopping (5)

No 122

Across

1 Beginning (8)
5 Small drink of whisky (4)
8 Greenish-bronze fish (5)
9 Timid (7)
10 Very long (7)
12 Stimulate a person (7)
14 Character in Hamlet (7)
16 Clinging shellfish (7)
18 Percussion musician (7)
19 Sudden movement (5)
20 Cloth worn around the waist (4)
21 Raise one's ___ : show surprise (8)

Down

1 Cries (4)
2 Prevents (6)
3 Watch (9)
4 Take small bites out of (6)
6 Prove to be false (6)
7 SE Asian country (8)
11 Disco (9)
12 Incorporates (8)
13 Love affairs (6)
14 Fish-eating bird of prey (6)
15 Rough shelter (4-2)
17 Insects that make honey (4)

No 123

Across

1 Create (4)
3 Recurring at intervals (8)
9 Eating grass (of cattle) (7)
10 One of the United Arab Emirates (5)
11 ___ Newton: English physicist (5)
12 Burst violently (7)
13 Large lizard (6)
15 Agreement or concord (6)
17 Least difficult (7)
18 Avoid (5)
20 Fortune-telling card (5)
21 Guardians (7)
22 Compliant; submissive (8)
23 Noble gas (4)

Down

1 Splendidly (13)
2 Australian marsupial (5)
4 Large birds of prey (6)
5 Freedom from control (12)
6 Doubtful (7)
7 British comic writer and comedian (5,8)
8 Unplugged (12)
14 Sudden increase (7)
16 Scattered about untidily (6)
19 Consent to (5)

No 124

Across

1 Character in the musical Oliver! (5)
4 Henry David ___ : US author and poet (7)
7 Bitterly pungent (5)
8 Old Dutch currency (pl) (8)
9 Caricature (5)
11 Follow another vehicle too closely (8)
15 Lengthen (8)
17 High-pitched cries (5)
19 Notes of a chord played in rapid succession (8)
20 Sully or blemish (5)
21 Warship (7)
22 Strong ringing sound (5)

Down

1 Disobediently (9)
2 African country with capital Windhoek (7)
3 Golfing measure of distance (7)
4 Desire for water (6)
5 List of ingredients for a dish (6)
6 ___ acid: protein building block (5)
10 Preceding (9)
12 Acquire as an heir (7)
13 Spanish beverage (7)
14 Intelligence activity (6)
16 Immature insects (6)
18 Go in (5)

No 125

Across

1 Highest adult male singing voice (4)
3 Teacher (8)
9 Toxins (7)
10 Frenzied (5)
11 Clumsy person (3)
12 Furnish or supply (5)
13 Synthetic fabric (5)
15 Tropical fruit (5)
17 First Greek letter (5)
18 Female sheep (3)
19 Long-___ owl: bird (5)
20 Form of an element (7)
21 Longing (8)
22 ___ Ifans: Welsh actor (4)

Down

1 Suitably (13)
2 Person who steals (5)
4 Dreary (6)
5 Official praise (12)
6 Particular languages (7)
7 Open-mindedness (13)
8 Popular district in London (6,6)
14 Large retail stores (7)
16 Something done (6)
18 The beginning of an era (5)

No 126

Across

7 Symbolic (6)
8 Batting order (4-2)
9 Mischievous god in Norse mythology (4)
10 Restful (8)
11 Country in N Africa (7)
13 Surround and harass; beets (anag) (5)
15 Adhesive substance (5)
16 Make amends (7)
18 State of Australia (8)
19 Robert De ___ : actor (4)
21 Men's tight fitting hat (6)
22 Showy (6)

Down

1 Repetition of a sound (4)
2 Medication for allergies (13)
3 Sour in taste (7)
4 Craftily (5)
5 Wet behind the ears (13)
6 Most amusing (8)
12 With undiminished force (8)
14 Swells (7)
17 Alphabetical list (5)
20 Rough or harsh sound (4)

No 127

Across

1. Seem (6)
7. Stubbornness (8)
8. Muhammad ___ : boxer (3)
9. Group of mountains (6)
10. Close securely; aquatic mammal (4)
11. Speak without preparation (2-3)
13. Coolness (7)
15. Breathed in sharply (7)
17. Woollen fabric (5)
21. Supermodel married to David Bowie (4)
22. Goes round the edge of; garments (6)
23. Unit of weight (3)
24. Take away (8)
25. Sour to the taste (6)

Down

1. Deciduous flowering shrub (6)
2. Original (6)
3. Settle for sleep (of birds) (5)
4. Building (7)
5. Impressive manner of a person (8)
6. Large bodies of water (6)
12. Unending (8)
14. Type of polish (7)
16. Large dark cloud bearing rain (6)
18. Took it easy (6)
19. Relating to cultural and national origins (6)
20. View (5)

Across

1 US state (4)
3 Changing (8)
9 Plaited lock of hair (7)
10 Laud (5)
11 ___ out: be frugal with (3)
12 Escape from (5)
13 Make a physical or mental effort (5)
15 Stare (anag) (5)
17 Break out with force (5)
18 Cause friction (3)
19 Invigorating medicine (5)
20 Country in Africa (7)
21 Shows (8)
22 Sort; variety (4)

Down

1 Unparalleled (13)
2 Single-celled plants (5)
4 Remove; excise (6)
5 Decide in advance (12)
6 Trespass (7)
7 50th anniversary of a major event (6,7)
8 Relating to numbers (12)
14 Former student (7)
16 Of inferior quality (6)
18 Popular sport (5)

No 129

Across

1 Repeat (6)
4 Eventual outcome (6)
9 Device attached to a door (7)
10 Container releasing a fine spray (7)
11 Sound of any kind (5)
12 Make available for sale (5)
14 Edward ___ : former Prime Minister (5)
15 Church farmland (5)
17 Mediterranean island country (5)
18 Guglielmo ___ : radio pioneer (7)
20 Eight-sided polygon (7)
21 Notoriety (6)
22 Marked with small spots (6)

Down

1 Gathering up leaves in the garden (6)
2 Administrative division (8)
3 Foot joint (5)
5 Ancient Egyptian ruler (7)
6 Small shelters (4)
7 Bar that turns a rudder (6)
8 Instance of buying or selling (11)
13 Small window (8)
14 Great courage (7)
15 Third sign of the zodiac (6)
16 Gained deservedly (6)
17 Saying; slogan (5)
19 Ridge of rock (4)

Across

1 Discard (8)
5 Imitated (4)
9 Rigid (5)
10 Freight (5)
11 Roundabout (10)
14 Living things (6)
15 Invalidate (6)
17 Build up (10)
20 Gena Lee ___ : Baywatch actress (5)
21 Landowner (5)
22 Mud (4)
23 Two-wheeled vehicles (8)

Down

1 Tease (4)
2 Work hard (4)
3 Action of breaking a law (12)
4 Workplace (6)
6 Individual; private (8)
7 Porch (8)
8 Not on purpose (12)
12 Got hold of (8)
13 Round (8)
16 Opposite of an acid (6)
18 Tablet (4)
19 Chances of winning (4)

No 131

Across

1 Animal enclosure (4)
3 Scholarly (8)
9 Person proposed for office (7)
10 Elevated step (5)
11 Newt (3)
12 Not heavy (5)
13 Cuban folk dance (5)
15 Suffuse with colour (5)
17 Tines (anag) (5)
18 Part of a curve (3)
19 Run away with a lover (5)
20 Not limited to one class (7)
21 Christmas season (8)
22 Pottery material (4)

Down

1 Successively (13)
2 The entire scale (5)
4 Belief in a god or gods (6)
5 Action of moving a thing from its position (12)
6 Citrus fruits (7)
7 Tactically (13)
8 Sporadic (12)
14 Plunder (7)
16 Moved (6)
18 Pertaining to the ear (5)

No 132

Across

8 Square dance (9)
9 Pair of actors (3)
10 Fourth month (5)
11 Tightly framed camera shot (5-2)
12 Opposite of shortest (7)
13 Dull heavy sound (4)
17 Baby beds (4)
18 Doing as one is told (7)
22 Responded to (7)
24 Pointed projectile (5)
25 Consume food (3)
26 Useful services (9)

Down

1 Crouch (5)
2 Put into action (5,3)
3 Group of three plays (7)
4 Pieces of bread (6)
5 Heavy noble gas (5)
6 Axelike tool (4)
7 Submarine weapon (7)
14 Banister (8)
15 Accumulated over time (7)
16 Monumental Egyptian structure (7)
19 Small parrot (informal) (6)
20 Swagger (5)
21 Joe ___ : English presenter and actor (5)
23 Poker stake (4)

No 133

Across

1 Destiny (4)
3 Large outbreak of a disease (8)
9 Fatty substance (7)
10 Large fruit with pulpy flesh (5)
11 Sceptic (5)
12 Japanese dish of raw fish (7)
13 Lightweight garment (1-5)
15 Short tune used in advertising (6)
17 Followed behind (7)
18 Capital of Ghana (5)
20 Solemn promises (5)
21 Do repeatedly (7)
22 Ominous (8)
23 Fill or satiate (4)

Down

1 Congratulations (13)
2 Mortise partner (5)
4 Subject to a penalty (6)
5 Tamed (12)
6 Stage in brewing (7)
7 In a thoughtful manner (13)
8 Decomposition by a current (12)
14 Cheer (7)
16 Regard with approval (6)
19 Move on hands and knees (5)

No 134

Across

1 Anniversary of when you are born (8)
5 Sharp nail as on a cat (4)
8 Do really well at (5)
9 Brazilian dance (7)
10 Prodding with the elbow (7)
12 Inclined (7)
14 At all times (7)
16 All together (2,5)
18 Mundane (7)
19 Humiliate (5)
20 Throb (4)
21 Space rock (8)

Down

1 Exhaled air (4)
2 Excessively ornate (of music) (6)
3 Extremely funny (9)
4 In poor health (6)
6 Introduction (4-2)
7 Person engaging in a complicated dispute (8)
11 Express disapproval (9)
12 Flowering plant (5,3)
13 Not rough (6)
14 Barriers between houses (6)
15 Fierce or domineering woman (6)
17 Long-running dispute (4)

No 135

Across

1 Built (11)
9 Valuable thing (5)
10 SI unit of illuminance (3)
11 Dreadful (5)
12 Benefactor (5)
13 On the shore of a sea (8)
16 Small streams (8)
18 Irritates (5)
21 Ballroom dance (5)
22 Negative vote (3)
23 Remote in manner (5)
24 Study of lawbreaking (11)

Down

2 Sets of clothes (7)
3 Swift-flying songbird (7)
4 World's largest country (6)
5 Quoted (5)
6 ___ DeGeneres: US comedienne (5)
7 Questioning a statement (11)
8 Sayings (11)
14 Injurious (7)
15 Large cushion for sitting on (7)
17 Innate (6)
19 Relay (anag) (5)
20 Group of bees (5)

Across

1 Plaster for coating walls (6)
7 Shrill (8)
8 Made-up statement (3)
9 Deer horn (6)
10 A group of three people (4)
11 Pastoral poem (5)
13 Played for time (7)
15 Critical (7)
17 Test or examine a metal (5)
21 The Orient (4)
22 Seaport in N Spain (6)
23 Eg Hedwig in Harry Potter (3)
24 Sledge (8)
25 Phantoms (6)

Down

1 Italian sausage (6)
2 Anxious (6)
3 Quartzlike gems (5)
4 Place out of sight (7)
5 Coal containers (8)
6 Ask a person to come (6)
12 Style of speech (8)
14 Charles ___ : English mathematician (7)
16 Explanation (6)
18 Fires a bullet (6)
19 Gives in (6)
20 Bandage for an injured arm (5)

No 137

Across

1 Unwrap or untie (4)
3 Cheeky (8)
9 Giving off light (7)
10 Traffic light colour (5)
11 Mother (3)
12 Jewelled headdress (5)
13 Command (5)
15 Theme for a discussion (5)
17 Lift with effort (5)
18 ___ Titmuss: TV personality (3)
19 Browned bread (5)
20 Desiring what someone else has (7)
21 Making less clear (8)
22 Impose a tax (4)

Down

1 Uncaring (13)
2 Belief in a creator (5)
4 Accosted; robbed (6)
5 Ugly (12)
6 Clasp (7)
7 Menacingly (13)
8 Unhappy (12)
14 Boastful behaviour (7)
16 Clay ___ : shooting target (6)
18 Similar (5)

Across

1 Experiencing violent anger (6)
4 Packed carefully and neatly (6)
9 Inactive pill (7)
10 Tranquil (7)
11 Low dull sounds (5)
12 Flowers (5)
14 Small bottles (5)
15 Soar; rush (5)
17 Thin crisp biscuit (5)
18 Italian sports car (7)
20 Hitting (7)
21 Servant in a noble household (6)
22 Altitude (6)

Down

1 Hold in high esteem (6)
2 Grainy (8)
3 Requirements (5)
5 Tough questions (7)
6 Predatory canine mammal (4)
7 Bores into (6)
8 Type of artist (11)
13 Moving location (8)
14 Porch (7)
15 Gently (6)
16 Intense feeling of fear (6)
17 Produce a literary work (5)
19 Repeat (4)

No 139

Across

1 In an abundant and lush manner (11)
9 Pierced by a bull's horn (5)
10 Sticky substance (3)
11 Wash with clean water (5)
12 Ancient object (5)
13 Happen simultaneously (8)
16 Altercation (8)
18 Favouring extreme views (5)
21 Stadium (5)
22 Strong alkaline solution (3)
23 Edible pungent bulb (5)
24 Fear in front of an audience (5,6)

Down

2 Object used in the kitchen (7)
3 Necessity (7)
4 An advance; progress (6)
5 Lowest point (5)
6 Allowed by official rules (5)
7 Awfully (11)
8 Give your full attention to (11)
14 Film about a magical board game (7)
15 Next after sixth (7)
17 Respite (6)
19 Bird sound; chirp (5)
20 With a forward motion (5)

Across

1 European mountain range (4)
3 Calm and free from strife (8)
9 Unit of sound in a language (7)
10 The Norwegian language (5)
11 Gradual reduction in value (12)
14 Pouch; enclosed space (3)
16 Not illuminated (5)
17 Uncooked (of meat) (3)
18 Swimming technique (12)
21 Door hanger (5)
22 Chocolate chewy cake (7)
23 Intentionally hidden (8)
24 Appends (4)

Down

1 Hand clapping (8)
2 Camera image (5)
4 First woman (3)
5 Person's physical state (12)
6 Passion (7)
7 Told an untruth (4)
8 The proprietor of an eating establishment (12)
12 Flatten on impact (5)
13 Small pincers (8)
15 Small crown (7)
19 Possessed (5)
20 You (archaic) (4)
22 Disapproving sound (3)

No 141

Across

1 Stargazers (11)
9 Group of eight (5)
10 Trap; ensnare (3)
11 Stares with the mouth wide open (5)
12 Small house (5)
13 Squashed (8)
16 Neat and smart (5-3)
18 Religious acts (5)
21 Most respected person in a field (5)
22 Anecdotes about a person (3)
23 Pale brownish-yellow colour (5)
24 Science of communications (11)

Down

2 Excess (7)
3 Male chicken (7)
4 See (6)
5 Roadside form of lodging (5)
6 Stiff (5)
7 Dictatorial (11)
8 Comprehends (11)
14 Unrecoverable sum of money one is owed (3,4)
15 Man-made fibre (7)
17 Composite fungus and alga (6)
19 Sorrowful (5)
20 Twenty (5)

No 142

Across

1 Catherine ___ : British comedienne (4)
3 ___ stork: large bird (8)
9 Money owed that should have been paid (7)
10 From that time (5)
11 Form of humour (5)
12 Separated; remote (7)
13 Plan (6)
15 Capital of Lebanon (6)
17 Precisely (7)
18 Uniform jacket (5)
20 Small antelope (5)
21 Slender stemlike plant appendage (7)
22 Establish firmly (8)
23 Dairy product (4)

Down

1 Sausages baked in batter (4-2-3-4)
2 Trunk of the body (5)
4 Purify then condense (6)
5 Completely unaware of (12)
6 Shaped like a ring (7)
7 Conceptually (13)
8 Intricate and confusing (12)
14 War carriage (7)
16 Believer in the occult (6)
19 ___ Jones: American singer-songwriter (5)

No 143

Across

1. ___ man: type of biscuit (11)
9. Water container (5)
10. Top (anag) (3)
11. Passenger ship (5)
12. Long-legged bird (5)
13. Decorative designs (8)
16. Cause to feel isolated (8)
18. Suitably (5)
21. Drawing making up part of a cartoon strip (5)
22. Ovoid foodstuff (3)
23. Dry biscuits used as baby food (5)
24. Fit to be seen (11)

Down

2. Meaninglessness (7)
3. One of the archangels (7)
4. Step down from a job (6)
5. Rejuvenate (5)
6. Prevent (5)
7. In a state of disrepair (11)
8. Narrator (11)
14. Part of the ocean (4,3)
15. Hurtful (7)
17. Make less tight (6)
19. Big cat (5)
20. Threads or fibres (5)

No 144

Across

1 Facial feature (4)
3 Awesome (8)
9 Couple (7)
10 Female parent (5)
11 Unpleasant giants (5)
12 Warning device for ships (7)
13 Writer (6)
15 Adhesive putty (6)
17 Frozen water spears (7)
18 Country once ruled by Papa Doc (5)
20 Type of stopwatch (5)
21 Reveal (7)
22 Act of sticking together (8)
23 Blue-green colour (4)

Down

1 Patriotic (13)
2 Track of an animal (5)
4 Unique (3-3)
5 Data about a population (12)
6 Distant settlement (7)
7 Young person (6,7)
8 Upper chamber in Parliament (5,2,5)
14 Victory (7)
16 Old Portuguese currency (6)
19 Creamy-white colour (5)

Across

8 Capital of Slovenia (9)
9 That vessel (3)
10 Rocky (5)
11 Hates (7)
12 Loving deeply (7)
13 ___ Lendl: former tennis star (4)
17 British nobleman (4)
18 Trying experiences (7)
22 Male witch (7)
24 Lag behind (5)
25 Annoy constantly (3)
26 Scheming; acting deceitfully (9)

Down

1 Grasp tightly (5)
2 Taxonomic group (8)
3 Game participants (7)
4 Forgive (6)
5 People not ordained (5)
6 Poses a question (4)
7 Stopping (7)
14 Explosively unstable (8)
15 Beverage made from grapes (3,4)
16 Trace of something (7)
19 Having a jaunty appearance (6)
20 Feelings and emotions (5)
21 Nick ___ : Liberal Democrat politician (5)
23 Road ___ : anger when driving (4)

No 146

Across

1 Assumed proposition (5)
4 Spread out (5)
10 ___ to: disagreeing with (7)
11 Religious table (5)
12 Pairs of people (4)
13 Opposite in meaning (8)
16 Peak (6)
17 Economise (6)
20 Imitate (8)
21 Animal's den (4)
23 Seed-eating songbird (5)
25 Cure-alls (7)
26 Item of cutlery (5)
27 Come to a place with (5)

Down

2 Brass musical instrument (9)
3 Vertical spar on a ship (4)
5 Custom (8)
6 Creative activity (3)
7 Scandinavian (6)
8 Supplementary component (3-2)
9 Address a deity (4)
14 State of excitement (9)
15 Outcry (8)
18 Rot or decay (of food) (6)
19 Opposite one of two (5)
20 Strain (4)
22 Platform leading out to sea (4)
24 Quick sleep (3)

No 147

Across

1 The back of the neck (6)
7 Favourably disposed towards (8)
8 Grey-brown colour (3)
9 Poor district of a city (6)
10 Dull car sound (4)
11 Anxious (5)
13 Rebuttal (7)
15 Carbon ___ : greenhouse gas (7)
17 Loft (5)
21 Short tail (4)
22 Cower; recoil (6)
23 At this moment (3)
24 Everlasting (8)
25 Sailing vessels (6)

Down

1 Abrupt (6)
2 Park keeper (6)
3 Ten more than forty (5)
4 Light two-wheeled motor vehicle (7)
5 Noble title (8)
6 Source of caviar (6)
12 Annoyance (8)
14 Teach (7)
16 Money received (6)
18 Deep pit (6)
19 Moves like a baby (6)
20 Mountainous (5)

No 148

Across

1 Capable of being used (8)
5 Emperor of Rome 54-68 (4)
9 Be alive; be real (5)
10 Courage; boldness (5)
11 Lose one's job (3,3,4)
14 Attribute to (6)
15 Modifies (6)
17 Cocktail containing pineapple juice (4,6)
20 Breathe out loudly (5)
21 Hawaiian greeting (5)
22 Shallow food container (4)
23 Person of varied learning (8)

Down

1 Follow orders (4)
2 Mire (anag) (4)
3 Establish as genuine (12)
4 Extremes (6)
6 Grounding (of electricity) (8)
7 Bridge above another road (8)
8 Middleman (12)
12 Inclined or willing (8)
13 Views about something (8)
16 Lacking in pigmentation (6)
18 Closing section of music (4)
19 Clean with water (4)

No 149

Across

1 Land surrounded by water (4)
3 Agitated (8)
9 Exerts control over (7)
10 Smart; ache (5)
11 Violate a law of God (3)
12 Prevent (5)
13 Approaches (5)
15 Produce eggs (5)
17 Rocky; harsh (5)
18 Possesses (3)
19 Piece of furniture (5)
20 Make bigger (7)
21 Reaction (anag) (8)
22 Small vipers (4)

Down

1 Peculiar or individual (13)
2 Attractive flower (5)
4 Instrument panel of a car (6)
5 Untimely (12)
6 Ancient war galley (7)
7 Virtuousness (13)
8 Amazement (12)
14 Not varying (7)
16 Ratio of reflected to incident light (6)
18 Aromatic plants (5)

No 150

Across
1 Eg beef or pork (4)
3 Not usual (8)
9 Painting medium (7)
10 Killer whales (5)
11 Place of conflict (12)
13 Revels (anag) (6)
15 Stationary part of a motor (6)
17 Characteristic of the present (12)
20 US state (5)
21 Understand (7)
22 Household implements (8)
23 Gets married (4)

Down
1 Put into long-term storage (8)
2 Allow entry to (5)
4 Strong ringing sounds (6)
5 Commensurate (12)
6 Seed with a fibrous husk and edible white flesh (7)
7 Tilt to one side (4)
8 Formal announcements (12)
12 Dreariness (8)
14 Break an agreement (7)
16 Without ethics (6)
18 Stand up (5)
19 In ___ : instead (4)

No 151

Across

1 Gives a description of (6)
7 Trifling (8)
8 Opposite of bottom (3)
9 Not awake (6)
10 Level and regular (4)
11 Pure love (5)
13 Characteristics (7)
15 Decorative altar cloth (7)
17 Willow twig (5)
21 Too; in addition (4)
22 Avoided (6)
23 Cease (3)
24 Roman building (8)
25 Hamper (6)

Down

1 Surface film; coating (6)
2 African antelope (6)
3 Watched secretly (5)
4 Used for storing fat (of body tissue) (7)
5 Supporting railway track beams (8)
6 Cause to fall from a horse (6)
12 Scaly anteater (8)
14 Cheese on toast (7)
16 Refill (6)
18 In truth; really (6)
19 Steering mechanism of a boat (6)
20 ___ Harding: Girls Aloud singer (5)

No 152

Across
1 Bubble violently (6)
4 Weakly (6)
9 Fast musical composition (7)
10 John ___ : tennis player (7)
11 Natural satellites (5)
12 Manages (5)
14 Small boat (5)
15 Household garbage (5)
17 Public square (5)
18 Relating to knowledge based on deduction (1,6)
20 Starting points (7)
21 Images (anag) (6)
22 Mythical male sea creatures (6)

Down
1 Plant with oil rich seeds (6)
2 Country in NE Africa (8)
3 Injures (5)
5 Intrinsic nature (7)
6 Ale (4)
7 Songlike cries (6)
8 Mixture (11)
13 Representative example (8)
14 Selects (7)
15 Emotional shock (6)
16 Dried grape (6)
17 Item won in a competition (5)
19 Wander (4)

No 153

Across

1 Egyptian goddess of fertility (4)
3 Greeted warmly (8)
9 One who assesses metals (7)
10 Strong desires (5)
11 Joke (3)
12 Walk heavily and firmly (5)
13 Alcoholic beverage (5)
15 U-shaped curve in a river (5)
17 Smooth textile fibre (5)
18 Vessel; jolt (3)
19 Foresee or predict (5)
20 Language spoken in Rome (7)
21 Extremely happy (8)
22 Inflammation of an eyelid (4)

Down

1 Not proper (13)
2 Henrik ___ : Norwegian author (5)
4 Short trip to perform a task (6)
5 Female fellow national (12)
6 Wealthy businessperson (7)
7 Act of vanishing (13)
8 Valetudinarianism (12)
14 Sea journeys (7)
16 Swimming costume (6)
18 Shared by two or more people (5)

No 154

Across

1 Enter unlawfully (8)
5 Crustacean (4)
9 Lucid (5)
10 Not suitable in the circumstances (5)
11 Analogy (10)
14 Wrote (6)
15 Refrains from injuring (6)
17 Disparity (10)
20 Tiny crustaceans (5)
21 Make less sharp (5)
22 Energy and enthusiasm (4)
23 Navigating (8)

Down

1 Short nail (4)
2 Days before major events (4)
3 Resolutely (12)
4 Angel of the highest order (6)
6 Assimilate again (8)
7 Person who studies plants (8)
8 Discreditable (12)
12 Scatter in drops (8)
13 Aromatic plant used in cooking (8)
16 Celestial body (6)
18 German car manufacturer (4)
19 Adult male deer (4)

No 155

Across

1 Large cask (8)
5 Freezes over (4)
8 Baked custard desserts (5)
9 Edges (7)
10 Four-stringed guitar (7)
12 Guest (7)
14 Eg Iceland and Borneo (7)
16 Cowboy hat (7)
18 Slanting (7)
19 Harsh and grating in sound (5)
20 Team (4)
21 School pupils (8)

Down

1 High fidelity (abbrev) (2-2)
2 Diagrams (6)
3 Institutions providing healthcare (9)
4 Plant framework; bower (6)
6 Masticated (6)
7 Stops temporarily (8)
11 Not changed (9)
12 Variants (8)
13 Cut down a tree (6)
14 Force fluid into (6)
15 Liam ___ : Irish actor (6)
17 Sight organs (4)

No 156

Across

1 Caribbean country (4)
3 Explicit (8)
9 Sailor (7)
10 Silk dress fabric (5)
11 Loathe (5)
12 Mournful (7)
13 Purpose (6)
15 A size of book page (6)
17 Loudly (7)
18 Ben ___ : Scottish mountain (5)
20 ___ couture: expensive clothes (5)
21 Supervise (7)
22 Repute; standing (8)
23 Greek god of war (4)

Down

1 Friendship (13)
2 Time when life begins (5)
4 Items used to carry money (6)
5 Effects or results (12)
6 More amusing (7)
7 Awareness (13)
8 Inflexible (12)
14 Commendation (7)
16 Being with organic and cybernetic parts (6)
19 Movable helmet part (5)

No 157

Across

1 Chamber of the heart (6)
5 Opposite of after (6)
8 Children (4)
9 Greek philosopher (8)
10 Evade (5)
11 Icy (7)
14 Successful and eminent (13)
16 Sterile (7)
18 Fissures (5)
20 Secondary personality (5,3)
22 ___ Barrymore: Hollywood actress (4)
23 Capital of New South Wales (6)
24 Swollen edible root (6)

Down

2 Groups of three books (9)
3 Clear perception (7)
4 Pulp (4)
5 Rod-shaped bacterium (8)
6 Old French currency (5)
7 Fish eggs (3)
12 Watchfulness (9)
13 Improbable (8)
15 Lost grip (7)
17 Smooth; groom (5)
19 Performer of an action (4)
21 Put down (3)

No 158

Across

1 Edge or border (5)
4 Ahead of time (5)
10 Get back together (7)
11 Detection technology (5)
12 Total spread of a bridge (4)
13 Substantial; not elusive (8)
16 Wooer (6)
17 Less fresh (of bread) (6)
20 Warriors (8)
21 Cow meat (4)
23 Radon (anag) (5)
25 Bursting (7)
26 Alloy of copper and zinc (5)
27 Wander off track (5)

Down

2 Instructing (9)
3 Harsh and miserable (4)
5 Annul or abolish (8)
6 Boy (3)
7 Comes up (6)
8 Floral leaf (5)
9 Correct; accurate (4)
14 Female dancer (9)
15 Omens (8)
18 Safe place (6)
19 Clutches tightly (5)
20 Body fat (4)
22 Facial blemish (4)
24 Blade for rowing a boat (3)

No 159

Across

1 Very informal phrases (5)
4 Labouring (7)
7 Modify (5)
8 Coaches (8)
9 Precious stone (5)
11 Covering in paper (8)
15 Someone paddling a light boat (8)
17 Wards (anag) (5)
19 Apparatus for hoisting loads (8)
20 Accumulate (5)
21 Active part of a fire (7)
22 County in England (5)

Down

1 Opposite of northward (9)
2 Yearbook (7)
3 Father of a parent (7)
4 Network of rabbit burrows (6)
5 Organ (6)
6 Chilly (5)
10 Mail slot (6,3)
12 Like a crow (7)
13 People harmed by criminal acts (7)
14 Distorts (6)
16 Not sinking (6)
18 Lover of Juliet (5)

No 160

Across

1 The spirit or soul (6)
5 Small finch (6)
8 Nought (4)
9 Newborn children (8)
10 Threshing tool (5)
11 Talented (7)
14 Thoughtless (13)
16 Diffusion of molecules through a membrane (7)
18 Examines quickly (5)
20 Sorriest (anag.) (8)
22 Song for a solo voice (4)
23 Formed an opinion about (6)
24 Evil spirits (6)

Down

2 Young plants (9)
3 Spicy Spanish sausage (7)
4 Sea eagle (4)
5 Enclosure formed from upright stakes (8)
6 Will (5)
7 Anger (3)
12 Addition to a building (9)
13 Aided (8)
15 Get back (7)
17 Outstanding (of a debt) (5)
19 Network of lines (4)
21 Flightless bird (3)

No 161

Across

1. Inexpensive restaurant (6)
4. Oxford ___ : famous London road (6)
9. Things that evoke reactions (7)
10. Bizarre (7)
11. Sense experience (5)
12. These keep your feet warm (5)
14. Telephones (5)
15. An easy task (5)
17. Spiny yellow-flowered shrub (5)
18. Kettledrums (7)
20. Flowers (7)
21. Roman military unit (6)
22. Expels air abruptly (6)

Down

1. Attacks on all sides (6)
2. A division between people (8)
3. Moulin ___ : musical film (5)
5. Female big cat (7)
6. Verge (4)
7. Pieces of furniture (6)
8. Action of ending a partnership (11)
13. Delightful and charismatic (8)
14. One who breaks the rules (7)
15. ___ acid: lemon juice constituent (6)
16. ___ up: botches or bungles (6)
17. Type of lizard (5)
19. Wire lattice (4)

164

Across

1 Throw a coin in the air (4)
3 Cartographer (8)
9 Theft of property (7)
10 Play a guitar (5)
11 Cry of a cat or gull (3)
12 First Pope (5)
13 Bring down (5)
15 Became less severe (5)
17 Town in Surrey; sheer (anag) (5)
18 Chopping tool (3)
19 Visual representation (5)
20 Long locks of hair (7)
21 Study of heredity (8)
22 Jealousy (4)

Down

1 Advertising by telephone (13)
2 Type of small fastener (5)
4 In a careless manner (6)
5 Made in bulk (4-8)
6 Protein found in hair (7)
7 Pitilessly (13)
8 Total confusion (12)
14 Sheikdom in the Persian Gulf (7)
16 Not moving (6)
18 Crime of setting something on fire (5)

No 163

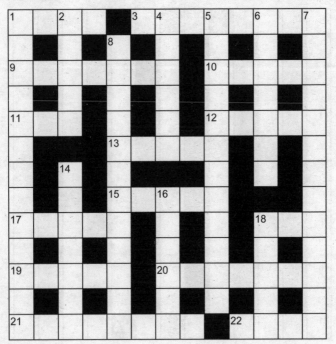

Across

1 Knocks lightly (4)
3 Arithmetic operation (8)
9 Irreverence (7)
10 Craftsman who uses stone (5)
11 Auction item (3)
12 Expect to happen (5)
13 Heroic tales (5)
15 Sweetener (5)
17 Seven (anag) (5)
18 Unhappy (3)
19 Recycle (5)
20 Edible jelly (7)
21 Flower-shaped competition awards (8)
22 Point of intersection (4)

Down

1 Simple problem-solving method (5,3,5)
2 Songbird (5)
4 Eg using a towel (6)
5 Limitless (12)
6 Install (7)
7 Failure to be present at (13)
8 Re-evaluation (12)
14 Winged angelic beings (7)
16 Snicker (6)
18 Fight (3-2)

No 164

Across

1 Freshest (6)
4 Sayings (6)
9 Word having the same meaning as another (7)
10 Eg crosswords and sudoku (7)
11 Unshapely masses (5)
12 Smallest quantity (5)
14 Select class (5)
15 Heaps (5)
17 Yellow-green colour; small fruit (5)
18 Capital of Northern Ireland (7)
20 Medicated tablet (7)
21 Fussy (6)
22 Promotional material (6)

Down

1 Hold close (6)
2 Grinding machine with sails (8)
3 Transmits (5)
5 Very light rain (7)
6 Ancient France (4)
7 Last light (6)
8 Restlessly (11)
13 Group of spectators (8)
14 Gets out (7)
15 Communal (6)
16 Dispirit (6)
17 Seeped (5)
19 Luxurious car (abbrev) (4)

No 165

Across

1 Change in appearance (11)
9 British nobles (5)
10 For each (3)
11 Not taut (5)
12 Spring flower (5)
13 Spend wastefully (8)
16 Casual and relaxed (8)
18 Published false statement (5)
21 Mark ___ : Samuel Langhorne Clemens (5)
22 Crux of a matter (3)
23 Arboreal primate (5)
24 Conjecture (11)

Down

2 Reassess financial worth (7)
3 Serviettes (7)
4 Sheepskin (6)
5 Enthusiasm (5)
6 Push away (5)
7 Very successful (of a book) (4-7)
8 Pollen traps (anag) (11)
14 Ballroom dance (7)
15 Ban on publication (7)
17 Standard; usual (6)
19 Type of jazz (5)
20 Sweet-scented shrub (5)

No 166

Across

1 Changing gradually (8)
5 Fencing sword (4)
9 Having three dimensions (5)
10 Lyres (5)
11 Complete cessation of taking a drug (4,6)
14 Stringed instrument (6)
15 Mammals; viragos (6)
17 Ban for breaking a rule (10)
20 Rafael ___ : Spanish tennis star (5)
21 Rental agreement (5)
22 Hearing organs (4)
23 Uses again (8)

Down

1 Engrave with acid (4)
2 Spheres (4)
3 Triumphantly (12)
4 No one (6)
6 Long-tailed parrot (8)
7 Author (8)
8 Considerately (12)
12 Proof of something (8)
13 Ponder (8)
16 Dress (6)
18 Roald ___ : author (4)
19 Opposite of more (4)

No 167

Across

1 Light in shade (4)
3 Obvious (8)
9 Salvaged (7)
10 Destiny; fate (5)
11 Peers (5)
12 Female big cat (7)
13 Inn (6)
15 ___ Cuthbert: actress (6)
17 Get too big for something (7)
18 Put out (5)
20 Needing to be scratched (5)
21 Imprecise (7)
22 Offered (8)
23 Depend on (4)

Down

1 One with extremely high standards (13)
2 Intense light beam (5)
4 Hawk (6)
5 Generally accepted (12)
6 People who make money (7)
7 Party lanterns (anag) (13)
8 Short story or poem for children (7,5)
14 Residence of the Pope (7)
16 For a short time (6)
19 Customary practice (5)

No 168

Across

1 Under (5)
4 Large sum of money (7)
7 Lacking meaning (5)
8 Close friend (8)
9 Land of a duke (5)
11 Usually (8)
15 Confused mixture (8)
17 Moves back and forth (5)
19 Austere people (8)
20 Nimble (5)
21 Made a garment by intertwining threads (7)
22 Sticky substance exuded by trees (5)

Down

1 Tasteless showiness (9)
2 Climbing tools (7)
3 Eg Tuesday (7)
4 Involving financial matters (6)
5 Language (6)
6 Between eighth and tenth (5)
10 Sailors of light vessels (9)
12 However (anag) (7)
13 Angular units (7)
14 Small hole (6)
16 Given out (6)
18 Four-wheeled vehicle (5)

No 169

Across

1 Dame (anag) (4)
3 Soft-bodied beetle (4-4)
9 Leaning at an angle (7)
10 Not telling the truth (5)
11 Throat of a voracious animal (3)
12 Golf clubs (5)
13 ___ Nash: writer of light verse (5)
15 Removes moisture (5)
17 Many-headed snake (5)
18 21st Greek letter (3)
19 Divide; separate (5)
20 Rude (7)
21 Showering with liquid (8)
22 Nervy (4)

Down

1 Process of transformation (of an insect) (13)
2 Softly radiant (5)
4 Fable (6)
5 Supporting cane (7,5)
6 River in South America (7)
7 Dictatorially (13)
8 Inharmoniously (12)
14 Violinist (7)
16 Call into question (6)
18 Eg covered with bricks (5)

No 170

Across

1 Multiply (11)
9 Makes beer (5)
10 Tree of the genus Ulmus (3)
11 Contrapuntal composition (5)
12 Republic in the Middle East (5)
13 Action of setting something on fire (8)
16 Wedge to keep an entrance open (8)
18 Wanderer (5)
21 Celestial body (5)
22 Label (3)
23 Five lines on which music is written (5)
24 Eg Huw Edwards and Trevor McDonald (11)

Down

2 Fixing; manipulating (7)
3 Freedom (7)
4 Wall painting or mural (6)
5 Tarnished (of a metal object) (5)
6 Unit of heat (5)
7 Keep cold (11)
8 Freed (11)
14 Continue (7)
15 Speak haltingly (7)
17 Flattened at the poles (6)
19 Not clearly stated (5)
20 Ascends (5)

Solutions

Puzzle 1
Puzzle 2
Puzzle 3

Puzzle 4
Puzzle 5
Puzzle 6

Puzzle 7
Puzzle 8
Puzzle 9

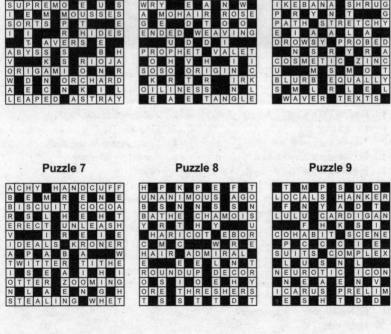

Solutions

Puzzle 10

Puzzle 11

Puzzle 12

Puzzle 13

Puzzle 14

Puzzle 15

Puzzle 16

Puzzle 17

Puzzle 18

Solutions

Puzzle 19

Puzzle 20

Puzzle 21

Puzzle 22

Puzzle 23

Puzzle 24

Puzzle 25

Puzzle 26

Puzzle 27

Solutions

Puzzle 28

Puzzle 29

Puzzle 30

Puzzle 31

Puzzle 32

Puzzle 33

Puzzle 34

Puzzle 35

Puzzle 36

Solutions

Puzzle 37

Puzzle 38

Puzzle 39

Puzzle 40

Puzzle 41

Puzzle 42

Puzzle 43

Puzzle 44

Puzzle 45

Solutions

Puzzle 46

```
 R E C O G N I T I O N
S   M   T   U   E   L   M
U   P   T H R U M   S P A
B R A V O   S   P   E   C
T   T   M   E   I N N E R
R E H E A R S E       O
A   Y   N       S A S   S
C       E L E C T R I C
T U F T S   A   O   T   O
I   A   I   V   F E D U P
N I B   G R I E F   E   I
G   L   H   S   E   C   C
 P E N T A H E D R O N
```

Puzzle 47

```
   C   B   D   S   T   W
 D I L I G E N T   H E A D
   T   A   I   A   O   G
 G R A N   C A M E R O O N
   U   N   I   P   N
 I S S U I N G   G U I S E
     A   G C N
 S C A L D   C R Y S T A L
   H   S   I   E   B
 V E R B A T I M   T U B A
   R   O   A   S   E
 T R O N   T R O L L E Y S
   Y   D   E   N   E   S
```

Puzzle 48

```
H I G H   P R E M I E R E
A   A   C   E   O   S   N
L I F T O F F   U N C U T
F   F   M   U   N   H   E
H U E   M   S   T H E I R
E       O P E R A   W   T
A   P   N       I   S   A
R   L   W O M A N       I
T R A C E   I   S   V A N
E   T   L   I   I   O   M
D W E L L   I N D U L G E
L   A   T   E   E   G   N
Y O U T H F U L   C A S T
```

Puzzle 49

```
 R E S P O N S I B L E
A   C   I   U   C   O   C
C   L   Q U A S I   O I L
H A I K U   N   N   S   A
I   P   A   C   G L E A N
E S S E N C E S       D
V   E   T       S   V E
E       E D I T I O N S
M A I D S   R   A   U   T
E   O   T   O   R I C C I
N U N   E X P E L   H   N
T   I   E   I   E E E E
 A C U P U N C T U R E
```

Puzzle 50

```
 I N T O   H A R D N E S S
N   H   C   D   I   L   U
C A R R I E D   C H E E P
O   O   R   I   T   C   E
R O W   R   N   A L T E R
R   U   O U G H T   O   F
U   O   C       O   R   L
P   U   P P E R       U
T O T E M   O   S   A D O
I   C   U   L   H U   U
B R O I L   L O I T E R S
L   M   U   E   P   A   L
E V E N S O N G   E D D Y
```

Puzzle 51

```
C H U M S   B E S T R E W
O   N   T   U   R   X
N   I   E   R   V A L U E
D E F E N D E R   N   D
I   O   C   A   A C T E D
M E R C I F U L   E   G
E   M   L   E   R   R G
N   R   F U N C T I O N
T A M E D   N   O   P
L   T   S T A N D O F F
L I C I T   I   O   S   I
A   N   D   M   T   E
U S U A L L Y   Y I E L D
```

Puzzle 52

```
O P U S E S   B E R E F T
E   A   K   A   E   L
P R O M   I N C I S I O N
C   U   P   K   E
T H O R N   E D I T I O N
A   A   C   A   R
A N T I B A C T E R I A L
C   R   E   I   N
L E T T E R S   C O N G A
O   Y   T   T   U
P A R T T I M E   O A T S
W   A   N   A   U   A
U N C L O G   M U S I N G
```

Puzzle 53

```
I M M O D E S T   T A X I
N   E   E   L   I   C   N
K E M P T   E   N E I G H
S   O   E   E   C   D   U
      C R Y P T O G R A M
B   A   M   S   M   A   A
A L B E I T   O P T I O N
C   S   N   C   A   N   E
K O O K A B U R R A
F   L   B   A   M   E
L E V E L   O   B E A D Y
I   E   E   L   L L E
P O S E   L A D Y B I R D
```

Puzzle 54

```
S Y R I A   V I R T U E S
U   O   G   E   H   N
B   B   I   R   F U S S Y
J U B I L A N T   M   U
U   E   E   O   E B B E D
G A R G L I N G   S   E
A   Y   Y   A   D   L
T   P   D A I Q U I R I
E X I L E   D   V   N
Y   U   A D H E S I V E
A L A R M   L   D   A
E   A   E U E T
I M P L I E D   S C R E E
```

Solutions

Puzzle 55

Puzzle 56

Puzzle 57

Puzzle 58

Puzzle 59

Puzzle 60

Puzzle 61

Puzzle 62

Puzzle 63

Solutions

Puzzle 64

```
C I A O   I G N O R A N T
L   D   E   A   F   S   R
O R D I N A L   F O S S E
S   E   T   O   T   I   A
E A R T H   S C H I S M S
D   U   H   E   T   U
C L A S S Y   E R A S E R
I   R   I   T   E       E
R I T U A L S   C L E F T
C   I   S   E   O   R
U P S E T   T O R O N T O
I   T   I   S   D   I   V
T R E N C H E S   H E R E
```

Puzzle 65

```
A U R O R A   I G   I
U   E   M E M B R A N E
G A S   O   P   A   D
I   O P E N E R   N A I L
T   R   G   E   D   C
E N T R Y   A S S E R T S
    E   F   S   U
A S S A U L T   E R R O R
E   C   I   S   O   E
R E N T   G A T E A U   W
M   I   H   U   R I O
A L L O T T E D   K   R
Y   N   S   S Q U E A K
```

Puzzle 66

```
S O A P   M A L D I V E S
L   P   Q   M   E   I   P
E S P O U S E   L A S S O
I   L   I   L   I   C   R
G R E E N   L O C K O U T
H   T   E   A   S   S
T O F F E E   S T R E A M
O   O   S   R   E       A
F O R E S E E   S H O W N
H   A   E   A   S   U   S
A R G O N   C H E E T A H
N   E   C   T   N   E   I
D I S P E N S E   S N I P
```

Puzzle 67

```
P A C E   A N E C D O T E
U   I   C   E   O   U   A
B I V O U A C   N O T E S
L   R   T   C   F   Y
I N C O M P A T I B L E
C   U   R   L   O   F
L A I R D S   V I E W E R
Y   N   G   S   A   I
    U N D E T E C T A B L E
G   A   O   R   I   E   N
A P R O N   E V O L V E D
S   D   L   N   N   E   L
P U S S Y C A T   P L O Y
```

Puzzle 68

```
    D   R   S   A P   B
H E R O I C   C A R B O N
    M   L   H   H   O   O
W I L L   O V E R C A S T
    E   L   S   R   T
J O U R N A L   P A R I S
    V   C   R   C   S   N
D E P O T   C O T T A G E
    R   A   S   U   I
P H Y S I C A L   N A P S
    E   T   O   O   A   R
B A T E A U   M O T H E R
    D   R   T   B   E   Y
```

Puzzle 69

```
A B A T E D   G A L E N A
    E   R   U   I   O   E
E L L A   L E G A T E E S
    I   C   L   A   T
S T O K E   E N F O R C E
    T   E   V   T       A
F L I R T A T I O U S L Y
    E       L   C   N   L
I D Y L L I C   A C T O R
    E   D   F   O   U
E S P E C I A L   V E S T
    E   R   T   E   E   L
M E A S L Y   A R R A Y S
```

Puzzle 70

```
O D D S O N   S C A L A R
R   E   V   C   H   A   E
B U F F A L O   I   W   C
I   I   T   M E M E N T O
T I N G E   P   E   U
S   I   L   R E C A P
    T   D R A M A   O
C R E D O   I   N   C
A   S N   D E F E R
C A S S A V A   A   U   I
K   L   G   N E M E S I S
L   A   E   T   E   E   P
E M B O S S   A S I D E S
```

Puzzle 71

```
A U K S   M O C C A S I N
R   A   L   U   L   H   O
M E R R I E R   O D O U R
C   A   C   T   W   M
H A N D K E R C H I E F
A   E   A   E   R   B
I L K   T E N T S   S E A
R   N   Y   G   H       B
B O I S T E R O U S L Y
S   W   P   R   E   H
T W I L L   R I S O T T O
U   N   I   E   E   U   O
N E G A T I V E   S P U D
```

Puzzle 72

```
N O A H   R E S I S T E D
O   L   F   N   M   O   I
N O T I O N S   P E C K S
A   O   R   I   E   C   A
P O S I T   G A R L A N D
P   U   N   F   T   V
E U C L I D   N E V A D A
A   O   T   V   C   N
R A V I O L I   T R E A T
A   E   U   S   I   L   A
N O R M S   I R O N I N G
C   U   L   O   N   Z   E
E M P T Y I N G   C A R D
```

Solutions

Puzzle 73

Puzzle 74

Puzzle 75

Puzzle 76

Puzzle 77

Puzzle 78

Puzzle 79

Puzzle 80

Puzzle 81

Solutions

Puzzle 82

Puzzle 83

Puzzle 84

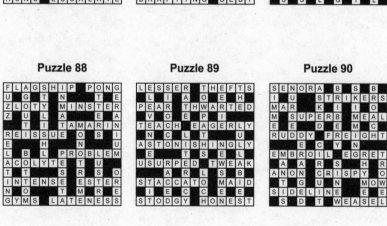

Puzzle 85

Puzzle 86

Puzzle 87

Puzzle 88

Puzzle 89

Puzzle 90

Solutions

Puzzle 91

```
U R S A . R E A S S U R E
N . O . B . I . I . K . N
J U D G I N G . M O R A L
U . A . B . H . I . A . I
S I S A L . T A L K I N G
T . . I . Y . A . N . H .
I N D O O R . U R G E N T
F . E . G . A . I . E . .
I M P E R I L . T I T A N
A . L . A . P . I . H . M
B L E E P . A V E R A G E
L . T . H . C . S . N . N
E V E R Y D A Y . M E L T
```

Puzzle 92

```
. A F F I R M A T I V E .
A . E . N . I . E . I . E
P . T . S O L A R . D I D
P I L A U . L . M E U . .
E . O . R E . S T O I C .
A N C I E N T S . . . A .
S . K . R . . C . C . T .
E . . C A L A M A R I . .
M I S T Y . S . L . R . .
E . A . E S . C A I R N .
N I L . A L I B I . B . A
T . S . R . G U . O . L .
. M A G N A N I M O U S .
```

Puzzle 93

```
U L N A . E F F L U E N T
N . O . T . A . I . N . A
I N V E R T S . F A C E S
N . A . A . T . E . L . T
T I E I N . E N S N A R E
E . . S . N . E . V . L .
L Y R I C S . I N H E R E
L . E . E . U . T . . S .
I N F A N T S . E A V E S
G . R . D . U . N . O . N
E R A S E . R E C E I V E
N . I . N . E . E . C . S
T I N C T U R E . J E T S
```

Puzzle 94

```
. L . S . V . A . T . K .
C U R T S I E D . A C I D
C . I . N . D . R . R . .
V E E R . T A L L N E S S
N . R . A . E . . C . . .
S T R I N G S . M O C H A
. N . . E . M . C . . . .
G O N G S . B A L C O N Y
R . . A . S . U . A . . .
E N D O R S E S . P U T S
A . C . T . I . A . I . .
I T C H . I N V E N T O R
E . E . R . E . T . N . .
```

Puzzle 95

```
R E S P E C T A B L E . .
R . R . O . O . U . I . M
E . R . C R A I G . V I E
S T A C K . S . E . I . A
T . T . E T . R A D O N .
A C I D T E S T . . I . .
U . C . S . . A . L . N .
R . . A M E N D I N G . .
A B A S H . A . A . M . L
N . M . O . N . L A P S E
T I P . U N I F Y . O . S
S . L . N . A . S . P . S
S Y N D I C A T I O N . .
```

Puzzle 96

```
Q U O T A . R E L A P S E
U . X . C . U . . S . M .
A . O . T . N . A S P I C
L I N G U I N E . A . T .
I . I . A . E . F I G H T
F R A C T U R E . E . M .
I . N . E . . L . D O W N T I M E
E . L . R I V E N . P . V . X .
N . E . N I N E T E E N
S C O W L . N . L . D .
U . A . E . O . U . A
P R A Y E R S . P U P I L
```

Puzzle 97

```
. F . W . D . N . . B . G
V I T A L I T Y . E R R S
N . N . L . M . T . . I .
H A R D . A L P H A B E T
L . E . T . H . . . V . .
L E A R N E R . H I R E D
E . . S . B . N . . . . .
S P I R E . S A R C A S M
O . . B . T . O . L . . .
R O O F L E S S . M A I L
R . I . N . M . I . C . .
C L O G . C L E A N S E R
Y . S . H . N . G . D . .
```

Puzzle 98

```
A D J U S T . A . T U G
I . C . P A N T O . L
O V E R A W E . N . O .
. I . R . N . A L L O W
E N T I C I N G . B . E
E . I . Y . H . O . R
P R I N T S . X E R X E S
U . N . Y . D . A . L
N . H . M I S D E E D S
C R I E R . C . L . E
H . B . O . E R A S E R S
U . I N L A Y . M . L
P A T . E . E P O N Y M
```

Puzzle 99

```
R O B S . O C C A S I O N
E . O . C . A . R . M . O
S L I T H E R . R I P E N
I . L . R . A . A . A . E
D I S T I N C T N E S S .
E . . S . H . G . S . R .
N U T . T H O S E . E Y E
T . H . M . I . M . . V .
. D I S A G R E E A B L E
A . S . S . . N . L . R .
B E T T E . J I T T E R S
L . L . V . O . S . N . E
E L E V E N T H . O D E S
```

Solutions

Puzzle 100

Puzzle 101

Puzzle 102

Puzzle 103

Puzzle 104

Puzzle 105

Puzzle 106

Puzzle 107

Puzzle 108

Solutions

Puzzle 109

Puzzle 110

Puzzle 111

Puzzle 112

Puzzle 113

Puzzle 114

Puzzle 115

Puzzle 116

Puzzle 117

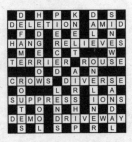

Solutions

Puzzle 118

Puzzle 119

Puzzle 120

Puzzle 121

Puzzle 122

Puzzle 123

Puzzle 124

Puzzle 125

Puzzle 126

Solutions

Puzzle 127

Puzzle 128

Puzzle 129

Puzzle 130

Puzzle 131

Puzzle 132

Puzzle 133

Puzzle 134

Puzzle 135

Solutions

Puzzle 136

Puzzle 137

Puzzle 138

Puzzle 139

Puzzle 140

Puzzle 141

Puzzle 142

Puzzle 143

Puzzle 144

Solutions

Puzzle 145

```
C S P P L A C
LJUBLJANA  SHE
A B A R I K A
STONY DETESTS
P R E O Y   I
 ADORING  IVAN
R E S   V O G
EARL ORDEALS
D M A S C C
WARLOCK TRAIL
I A O I N E
NAG DESIGNING
E E S H E C G
```

Puzzle 146

```
LEMMA  SPLAY
N U A A R R P
OPPOSED  ALTAR
R H T D C   A
DUOS CONTRARY
I N B N I G
CLIMAX  SCRIMP
U L O E T E
SIMULATE  LAIR
I Y H P T I
FINCH ELIXIRS
T A O R E O H
SPOON  BRING
```

Puzzle 147

Puzzle 148

```
OPERABLE  NERO
B M U I I A V
EXIST M NERVE
Y R H I T T R
 GETTHECHOP
D O N S R I A
IMPUTE  AMENDS
S I I A E G S
PINACOLADA
O I A B I C W
SNORT I ALOHA
E N E N R D S
DISH  POLYMATH
```

Puzzle 149

Puzzle 150

Puzzle 151

Puzzle 152

```
SEETHE  FEEBLY
E T U C S E O
SCHERZO  SEDD
A I T MCENROE
MOONS B N L
E P I  COPES
I  CANOE A
TRASH   R R
R O T PLAZA
APRIORI R D I
U O S ORIGINS
M V E N Z G I
AGEISM  MERMEN
```

Puzzle 153

```
ISIS WELCOMED
N B H R O A I
ASSAYER  URGES
P E P A N N A
PUN O N TRAMP
R CIDER T P
O V H Y E
P O OXBOW E A
RAYON I O  JAR
I A D K M O A
AUGUR ITALIAN
T E I N N N C
ECSTATIC  STYE
```

Solutions

Puzzle 154

Puzzle 155

Puzzle 156

Puzzle 157

Puzzle 158

Puzzle 159

Puzzle 160
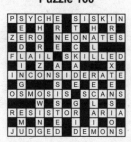

Puzzle 161

Puzzle 162

Solutions

Puzzle 163

Puzzle 164

Puzzle 165

Puzzle 166

Puzzle 167

Puzzle 168

Puzzle 169

Puzzle 170